CONTENTS

Pontius Pilate 2
John the Baptist 4
Mary and Elizabeth 8
Mary and Joseph 15
The Birth of Jesus 17
The Wise Men 21
The First Disciples 25
Wedding at Cana 27
Sermon on the Boat 30
Healing Miracles 34
A Tax Collector 36
Through the Roof 37
Lunch with Pharisee 40
Raising a Dead Boy 41
Feeding a Crowd 44
With the Disciples 46
Up to Jerusalem 47
The Devil Tempts Jesus 49
Transfiguration 51
Palm Sunday 53
Pharisee Meeting 59
Judas the Betrayer 60
The Last Supper 61
Garden of Gethsemane 69
Trial Before the Sanhedrin 73
Trial Before Pilate 79
On the Way to Golgotha 80
Jesus Crucified 92
Buried in a Tomb 96
The Empty Tomb 97
Jesus Appears to Many [illegible]9
The Last Big Fish Catc[illegible] [illegible]07
My Prayer [illegible]11
Matthew 5, 6, 7, [illegible]112
James 1, 2, 3, 4, ... 117
1 Peter 1, 2, 3, 4, ... 120
1 Corinthians 15 125
The Lost Son 128

In the year 30 A.D, the Roman Empire was 780 years old. It included all the countries around the Mediterranean, from Spain and Galatia to Egypt and Syria.
France
Spain
Italy
Rome
Greece
Syria
Africa
Palestine
Jerusalem
One day, in the palace of the Roman Governor Pilate who commanded the occupying forces,...
...located in Jerusalem; which was the capital of Judea in Palestine, and belonged to the Roman province of Syria.
Captain, what kind of news do you have in your weekly report?
Governor, I saw a large crowd of people at the Jordan river, where a certain John the Baptist is preaching. He's believed to be a prophet...
He baptizes people and talks about the coming of a new leader called the Messiah.
Mm...I see another leader, who'll recruit an army and try to drive us Romans, away...
It's not the first and won't be the last leader. But none has succeeded yet in driving us out!
Yes, these Jews are indeed a special people
They're the only people who cannot be broken... and Emperor Tiberias is giving in to them. When I had decorated this palace with golden paintings, displaying our Roman gods, he ordered me to remove them!

To these Jews this meant desecrating their holy city. Any pictures of their God are strictly forbidden. All our symbols, related to our Roman Empire are
considered blasphemous. Therefore, they made a complaint to Emperor Tiberias... and they won the case!
They're a difficult people to rule. My job as governor here in Jerusalem is the most unpleasant one in the whole empire!
That's right. These Jewish people are the only ones in the whole empire who don't have to worship our Roman gods!
They don't have to work on the Sabbath day and they're also permitted to refuse entry to their Temple to all non-Jewish people under the pretense of being a chosen people.
Oh, this Jerusalem temple! What a nightmare! When 200,000 pilgrims arrive for the Jewish feasts, one must be careful! Before you know it, they'll cause trouble and start a riot.
We're watching their movements from the Citadel Antonia and can prevent any trouble in time.
Allright, captain. Watch this Jordan river situation closely and keep me informed...
I'm going there myself. I know the Jewish authorities
are also wondering about this John the Baptist; they intend to make an investigation of their own...

Matthew 3: 1-17

In those days John the Baptist came, preaching in the Desert of Judea and saying, "Repent, for the kingdom of heaven is near." This is he who was spoken of through the prophet Isaiah: "A voice of one calling in the desert, 'Prepare the way for the Lord, make straight paths for him.' "

John's clothes were made of camel's hair, and he had a leather belt around his waist. His food was locusts

I immerse you into the water.
And I will lift you up, which means cleansing and renewing.
Meanwhile...
Are you not affected by what the prophet proclaims?
We don't need to change ourselves!
We are here to investigate for the Jewish authorities in Jerusalem, the High priest and the Pharisees.
Are you the man who is called: John the Baptist? Do you consider yourself the Christ?
No, I am not the Christ. I am not even worthy to untie His sandals.
Who are you then? Where do you come from? In whose name do you speak?
I am the voice of one calling in the desert: "Make straight the way for the Lord!"

and wild honey. People went out to him from Jerusalem and all Judea and the whole region of the Jordan. Confessing their sins, they were baptized by him in the Jordan River.
But when he saw many of the Pharisees and Sadducees coming to where he was baptizing, he said to them: "You brood of vipers! Who warned you to flee from the coming wrath? Produce fruit in keeping with repentance. And do not think you can say to yourselves, 'We have Abraham as our father.' I tell you that out of these stones God can raise up children for Abraham. The ax is already at the root of the trees, and every tree that does not produce good fruit will be cut down and thrown into the fire.

I baptize you with water for repentance. But after me will come one who is more powerful than I, whose sandals I am not fit to carry. He will baptize you with the Holy Spirit and with fire. His winnowing fork is in his hand, and he will clear his threshing floor, gathering his wheat into the barn and burning up the chaff with unquenchable fire."

Then Jesus came from Galilee to the Jordan to be baptized by John. But John tried to deter him, saying, "I need to be baptized by you, and do you come to me?"
Jesus replied, "Let it be so now; it is proper for us to do this to fulfill all righteousness." Then John consented.

As soon as Jesus was baptized, he went up out of the water. At that moment heaven was opened, and he saw the Spirit of God descending like a dove and lighting on him. And a voice from heaven said, "This is my Son, whom I love; with him I am well pleased."

Jesus was baptized in the Jordan river at the age of 30. Who was He? He was called the son of Joseph, the carpenter of Nazareth. His mother's name was Mary, a relative of the mother of John the Baptist. His parents could tell some wonderful things about the divine happenings which surrounded His birth.
Mary was engaged to be married to Joseph when she found herself pregnant
before they had been together... How did this happen?
One Sabbath day, Mary's parents return home from the synagogue.
You know the promise of the prophet Daniel! The angel Gabriel told him about the birth of the Messiah. I wonder if we shall experience that great day.
I believe it because...
...according to the prophecy of Daniel it should happen now, at this time!
Mary, go and fetch the lamp-oil and food for the meal, please...
Suddenly... Rejoice, Mary! You are highly favored by God!
What's happening? What are these greetings? Can it be that this is a message from heaven?
Fear not, Mary! You will be with child and give birth to a son and you are to call him: Jesus. He is the Messiah!

Luke 1: 26-38

In the sixth month, God sent the angel Gabriel to Nazareth, a town in Galilee, to a virgin pledged to be married to a man named Joseph, a descendant of David. The virgin's name was Mary. The angel went to her and said, "Greetings, you who are highly favored! The Lord is with you."
Mary was greatly troubled at his words and wondered what kind of greeting this might be. But the angel said to her, "Do not be afraid, Mary, you have found favor with God. You will be with child and give birth to a son, and you are to give him the name Jesus. He will be great and will be called the Son of the Most High. The Lord God will give him the throne of his father David, and he will reign over the house of Jacob forever; his kingdom will never end."
"How will this be," Mary asked the angel, "since I am a virgin?"
The angel answered, "The Holy Spirit will come upon you, and the power of the Most High will

I don't understand. How can I have a child, since I'm a virgin?
The Holy Spirit will come upon you and the power of the Most High will overshadow you. So the Holy One to be born will be called the Son of God. To prove that what I announced to you will happen: Elisabeth, your cousin is going to have a child in her old age. She, who was said to be barren, is in her sixth month. For nothing is impossible with God!
I'm the Lord's servant. May it be to me as you have said.
A few days later...
Mother, I'd like to spend some weeks with our cousin Elisabeth.
I see that you want this with all your heart, though you don't say why...
Your visit will surely make her happy as well as her husband Zacharias.
But they live far from here, in Judea.
You can only go if you join a caravan passing Nazareth on its way to Jerusalem.
But I'll put you in the care of a reliable guide, who'll look after you.
I'm not afraid, for I know that God will protect me!
Soon afterwards Mary is on her way to Judea.
God has blessed me with His presence and has spoken to me in my heart that I shall be the mother of the Messiah, Who will save us all from our sin. ...
I am curious as to how my cousin is doing and to find out that it is all true!
Mary from Nazareth, that's the way to Ain-Karin, where your cousin Elisabeth lives. The village is in that valley.
Thank you for the journey. May God protect you!

overshadow you. So the holy one to be born will be called the Son of God. Even Elizabeth your relative is going to have a child in her old age, and she who was said to be barren is in her sixth month. For nothing is impossible with God."
"I am the Lord's servant," Mary answered. "May it be to me as you have said." Then the angel left her.

Luke 1: 39-64

At that time Mary got ready and hurried to a town in the hill country of Judea, where she entered Zechariah's home and greeted Elizabeth. When Elizabeth heard Mary's greeting, the baby leaped in her womb, and Elizabeth was filled with the Holy Spirit. In a loud voice she exclaimed: "Blessed are you among women, and blessed is the child you will bear! But why am I so favored, that the mother of my Lord should come to me? As soon as the sound of your greeting reached my ears, the baby in my womb leaped for joy. Blessed is she who has believed that what the Lord has said to her will be accomplished!"

Then God's angel gave him a sign as proof: from that time on Zacharias was dumb.

Finally, there comes Zacharias!
He looks upset. Why does he make signs to us? As if he cannot speak all of a sudden...
..he must have seen a vision...
...or he received a revelation.
And now I'm six months pregnant.
How great is our God. He has taken away my disgrace...
Mary stayed three months with Elisabeth and returned home to Nazareth. The day came that Elisabeth gave birth to a son. On the eighth day they came to circumcise the child. At that occasion the child receives his name.
So, the circumcision is finished.
What name do you give this child?
He shall be called John.
A nice name! It means: The Lord is merciful.
But no-one in your family has that name!
And Mary said: "My soul glorifies the Lord and my spirit rejoices in God my Savior, for he has been mindful of the humble state of his servant. From now on all generations will call me blessed, for the Mighty One has done great things for me--holy is his name. His mercy extends to those who fear him, from generation to generation. He has performed mighty deeds with his arm; he has scattered those who are proud in their inmost thoughts. He has brought down rulers from their thrones but has lifted up the humble. He has

filled the hungry with good things but has sent the rich away empty. He has helped his servant Israel, remembering to be merciful to Abraham and his descendants forever, even as he said to our fathers."
Mary stayed with Elizabeth for about three months and then returned home.
When it was time for Elizabeth to have her baby, she gave birth to a son. Her neighbors and relatives heard that the Lord had shown her great mercy, and they shared her joy.

On the eighth day they came to circumcise the child, and they were going to name him after his father Zechariah, but his mother spoke up and said, "No! He is to be called John."
They said to her, "There is no one among your relatives who has that name."
Then they made signs to his father, to find out what he would like to name the child. He asked for a writing tablet, and to everyone's astonishment he wrote, "His name is John." Immediately his mouth was opened and his tongue was loosed, and he began to speak, praising God.

Matthew 1: 18-21

This is how the birth of Jesus Christ came about: His mother Mary was pledged to be married to Joseph, but

Upon wakening one morning...
What a strange dream!...
No doubt God has spoken to me through His angel!
I know Mary isn't lying. The child she expects is from God...
...and will be the Messiah,...
...who should be a descendant from King David!
Since Mary and I are descendants from David's royal family,...
...this child will be the fulfillment of prophecy.
Now I understand what God wants me to do!
I've made up my mind. I'll take Mary as my wife as soon as possible!
Soon after that, the wedding of Joseph and Mary is celebrated...
Mary, my beloved, welcome to this house. From now on it's yours too!

before they came together, she was found to be with child through the Holy Spirit. Because Joseph her husband was a righteous man and did not want to expose her to public disgrace, he had in mind to divorce her quietly.
But after he had considered this, an angel of the Lord appeared to him in a dream and said, "Joseph son of David, do not be afraid to take Mary home as your wife, because what is conceived in her is from the Holy Spirit. She will give birth to a son, and you are to give him the name Jesus, because he will save his people from their sins."

uke 2: 1:20

n those days Caesar Augustus issued a decree that a ensus should be taken of the entire Roman world. This was the first census that took place while uirinius was governor of Syria.) And everyone went his own town to register.

o Joseph also went up from the town of Nazareth in alilee to Judea, to Bethlehem the town of David, ecause he belonged to the house and line of David.

He went there to register with Mary, who was pledged to be married to him and was expecting a child. While they were there, the time came for the baby to be born, and she gave birth to her firstborn,

At the house of the relatives...
God bless you, my brothers!
Joseph! Welcome here, welcome!
May I introduce Mary, my wife? She expects her child soon. Where can we find a room for her?
I'm sorry! Our house is overcrowded. We have no place for you!
Joseph, follow my advise: Go into the stable. With the animals you'll be warm
That's a good idea. It will also be quiet there.
That night Mary gave birth to her first-born son...
She wrapped him in cloths and placed him in a manger...

a son. She wrapped him in cloths and placed him in a manger, because there was no room for them in the inn. And there were shepherds living out in the fields nearby, keeping watch over their flocks at night. An angel of the Lord appeared to them, and the glory of the Lord shone around them, and they were terrified. But the angel said to them, "Do not be afraid. I bring you good news of great joy that will be for all the people. Today in the town of David a Savior has been born to you; he is Christ the Lord. This will be a sign to you: You will find a baby wrapped in cloths and lying in a manger."

Suddenly a great company of the heavenly host appeared with the angel, praising God and saying, "Glory to God in the highest, and on earth peace to men on whom his favor rests."

When the angels had left them and gone into heaven, the shepherds said to one another, "Let's go to Bethlehem and see this thing that has happened, which the Lord has told us about."

So they hurried off and found Mary and Joseph, and the baby, who was lying in the manger. When they had seen him, they spread the word concerning what had been told them about this child, and all who heard it were amazed at what the shepherds said to them. But Mary treasured up all these things and pondered them in her heart. The shepherds returned, glorifying and praising God for all the things they had heard and seen, which were just as they had been told.

Luke 2: 22-38

When the time of their purification according to the Law of Moses had been completed, Joseph and Mary took him to Jerusalem to present him to the Lord (as is written in the Law of the Lord, "Every firstborn male is to be consecrated to the Lord"), and to offer a sacrifice in keeping with what is said in the Law of th Lord: "a pair of doves or two young pigeons."

Now there was a man in Jerusalem called Simeon, who was righteous and devout. He was waiting for th consolation of Israel, and the Holy Spirit was upon him. It had been revealed to him by the Holy Spirit that he would not die before he had seen the Lord's Christ. Moved by the Spirit, he went into the temple courts. When the parents brought in the child Jesus to do for him what the custom of the Law required, Simeon took him in his arms and praised God, saying

I bless this child, which...
..will cause the falling and the rising up of many people in all the world!
"Sovereign Lord, as you have promised, you now dismiss your servant in peace. For my eyes have seen your salvation, which you have prepared in the sight of all people, a light for revelation to the Gentiles and for glory to your people Israel." The child's father and mother marveled at what was said about him. 34Then Simeon blessed them and said to Mary, his mother: "This child is destined to cause the falling and rising of many in Israel, and to be a sign that will be spoken
Jesus' parents also remembered the events with the astronomers. That meeting showed how Jesus was welcomed by foreigners but rejected by his own people. At the time of Jesus' birth, there arrived in Jerusalem Magi (wise men) from the East...
Where's the new-born child, who'll be King of this nation?
We have seen his star appear in our countries.
What? Has the Messiah come?
Impossible! We would have known it in Jerusalem! But nobody has heard anything.
The King should hear this news immediately!

Majesty! Some foreigners are looking for a child, who is the promised Messiah!
They say that his birth has been shown through the position of the stars!
What? A child will be the Messiah and I was not informed? Secretly a rival to my throne is raised.
I have to be clever to uncover this new conspiracy!
Call the Pharisees at once!
I hear rumors about the arrival of the Messiah. I'll have to prepare for it. What do you know about his family and his birth-place?
The Holy Bible says: The Messiah will be a descendant of King David...
..and King David came from Bethlehem.
It is written: "Bethlehem, out of you will come the ruler who will be the shepherd of my people.
Quick, go and bring the wise men from the Orient here!
A little later...
I understand you're looking for a child, the Messiah?
Yes, we've seen his star!

against, so that the thoughts of many hearts will be revealed. And a sword will pierce your own soul too." There was also a prophetess, Anna, the daughter of Phanuel, of the tribe of Asher. She was very old; she had lived with her husband seven years after her marriage, and then was a widow until she was eighty-four. She never left the temple but worshiped night and day, fasting and praying. Coming up to them at that very moment, she gave thanks to God and spoke about the child to all who were looking forward to the redemption of Jerusalem.

tthew 2: 1-12

er Jesus was born in Bethlehem in Judea, during time of King Herod, Magi from the east came to ısalem and asked, "Where is the one who has been ı king of the Jews? We saw his star in the east and e come to worship him."

en King Herod heard this he was disturbed, and all ısalem with him. When he had called together all people's chief priests and teachers of the law, he asked them where the Christ was to be born. "In Bethlehem in Judea," they replied, "for this is what the prophet has written:

" 'But you, Bethlehem, in the land of Judah, are by no means least among the rulers of Judah; for out of you will come a ruler who will be the shepherd of my

While the days pass...King Herod is waiting in his palace...

These wise men still have not returned...

No doubt, they hid this descendant of David from me to rob me of my throne!
But I'll drench this conspiracy in blood!

Go with your soldiers to Bethlehem.. Look for all boys under two years in that town and surroundings. Show no mercy..kill them!

Mary, get up! We received a warning from heaven. The child is not safe here anymore!

We'll take the baby and leave immediately for Egypt!

After having been in exile for some time, Joseph and Mary returned to Nazareth in Galilee. There Jesus grew up and gained in wisdom while being obedient to his parents.
At the age of thirty, he went to John the Baptist and was baptized.

people Israel.'"
Then Herod called the Magi secretly and found out from them the exact time the star had appeared. He sent them to Bethlehem and said, "Go and make a careful search for the child. As soon as you find him, report to me, so that I too may go and worship him." After they had heard the king, they went on their way, and the star they had seen in the east went ahead of them until it stopped over the place where the child was. When they saw the star, they were overjoyed. On coming to the house, they saw the child with his mother Mary, and they bowed down and worshiped him. Then they opened their treasures and presented him with gifts of gold and of incense and of myrrh. And having been warned in a dream not to go back to Herod, they returned to their country by another route.

One day, John the Baptist sees Jesus passing by....
I tell both of you, my disciples, do you see that man?
He is the Lamb of God of whom is written: "Like a lamb he was led to the slaughter. He will take the sins of the world on Himself."
This means that He is the promised Messiah, the Christ!
Yes, I saw the Spirit of God come down from heaven on him...That is why I testify that He is the Son of God!
Come Andrew, we'll follow Him!
What do you look for?
Where do you live? We want to speak with you...
Come and see.
They spent considerable time with Him...
That was a heart-touching conversation.
I have to tell my brother Simon at once!
Simon! Simon! We found the Messiah! The Christ! Hurry up. I'll lead you to Him!
What? The Messiah? The Christ? Impossible!
You are Simon, the fisherman. You shall be called Peter. Follow Me!
Jesus, this is Philip, he's a friend of us... he's also from Bethsaida...
Philip, follow Me and become my disciple.
Philip went on his way, to tell a friend.

John 1: 29-42

The next day John saw Jesus coming toward him and said, "Look, the Lamb of God, who takes away the sin of the world! This is the one I meant when I said, 'A man who comes after me has surpassed me because he was before me.' I myself did not know him, but the reason I came baptizing with water was that he might be revealed to Israel."

Then John gave this testimony: "I saw the Spirit come down from heaven as a dove and remain on him. I would not have known him, except that the one who sent me to baptize with water told me, 'The man on whom you see the Spirit come down and remain is he who will baptize with the Holy Spirit.' I have seen and I testify that this is the Son of God."

The next day John was there again with two of his disciples. When he saw Jesus passing by, he said, "Look, the Lamb of God!"

When the two disciples heard him say this, they followed Jesus. Turning around, Jesus saw them follow-

ng and asked, "What do you want?"
They said, "Rabbi" (which means Teacher), "where are you staying?"
'Come," he replied, "and you will see."
So they went and saw where he was staying, and spent that day with him. It was about the tenth hour.
Andrew, Simon Peter's brother, was one of the two who heard what John had said and who had followed Jesus. The first thing Andrew did was to find his brother Simon and tell him, "We have found the Messiah" (that is, the Christ). And he brought him to Jesus.
Jesus looked at him and said, "You are Simon son of John. You will be called Cephas" (which, when translated, is Peter).

John 2: 1-11
On the third day a wedding took place at Cana in Galilee. Jesus' mother was there, and Jesus and his disciples had also been invited to the wedding. When the wine was gone, Jesus' mother said to him, "They have no more wine."
"Dear woman, why do you involve me?" Jesus replied, "My time has not yet come."
His mother said to the servants, "Do whatever he tells you."
Nearby stood six stone water jars, the kind used by the Jews for ceremonial washing, each holding from twenty to thirty gallons.
Jesus said to the servants, "Fill the jars with water"; so they filled them to the brim.
Then he told them, "Now draw some out and take it to

the master of the banquet."
They did so, and the master of the banquet tasted the water that had been turned into wine. He did not realize where it had come from, though the servants who had drawn the water knew. Then he called the bridegroom aside and said, "Everyone brings out the choice wine first and then the cheaper wine after the guests have had too much to drink; but you have saved the best till now."
This, the first of his miraculous signs, Jesus performed in Cana of Galilee. He thus revealed his glory, and his disciples put their faith in him.

Jesus travels to Capernaum on the shore of LakeGenasareth. John, Andrew and Peter work there as fishermen.
There are our fishing boats. This boat belongs to Simon...Peter.
My brother James and I, John, know the fishermen's trade.
You, fishermen, shall be my first disciples! Follow Me!
Everything is ready to start fishing tonight.
Jesus, you can spend the night in my house... my mother in law is ill, in bed with a high fever.
Let's go, Peter... Believe me, your mother in law will be healed!
I feel better! Yes, I feel very well. I'll get up and prepare some food for you.
That night Peter and his crew go fishing...

Luke 4: 38-40

Jesus left the synagogue and went to the home of Simon. Now Simon's mother-in-law was suffering from a high fever, and they asked Jesus to help her. So he bent over her and rebuked the fever, and it left her. She got up at once and began to wait on them. When the sun was setting, the people brought to Jesus all who had various kinds of sickness, and laying his hands on each one, he healed them.

The next morning....
What happened? My baskets are empty. Nothing for sale today?
We had an exhausting night, but caught nothing! Now we have to clean our nets.
There comes Jesus, followed by a crowd...
Peter, take your boat out a little so that I can talk to all these people who are eager to hear God's Word.
Jesus said: This is what the kingdom of God is like. A man scatters seed on the ground...
Night and day, whether he sleeps or is awake, the seeds sprout and grow...
..though he does not know how, all by itself the soil produces grain-first the stalk, then the head, then the full kerne in the head-producing our daily bread.
All of you are invited to enter! But you must change your lives! Your hearts should not be hard like a rock or like the soil filled with thorns, overgrown with desires for.....possessions, money and comforts!...

Luke 5: 1-11

One day as Jesus was standing by the Lake of Gennesaret,with the people crowding around him and listening to the word of God, he saw at the water's edge two boats, left there by the fishermen, who were washing their nets. He got into one of the boats, the one belonging to Simon, and asked him to put out a little from shore. Then he sat down and taught the people from the boat.
When he had finished speaking, he said to Simon, "Put out into deep water, and let down the nets for a catch."

Simon answered, "Master, we've worked hard all night and haven't caught anything. But because you say so, I will let down the nets."
When they had done so, they caught such a large number of fish that their nets began to break. So they signaled their partners in the other boat to come and help them, and they came and filled both

oats so full that they began to sink.
Vhen Simon Peter saw this, he fell at Jesus' knees and
aid, "Go away from me, Lord; I am a sinful man!" For
e and all his companions were astonished at the catch of
sh they had taken, and so were James and John, the
ons of Zebedee, Simon's partners.
hen Jesus said to Simon, "Don't be afraid; from now on
ou will catch men." So they pulled their boats up on
hore, left everything and followed him.

Jesus traveled through all of Galilee, preaching the Good News and healing the sick, crowds followed Him...
My time has come! The Kingdom of Heaven is near! It's knocking at your doors! Change your lives and turn to God and serve Him!
I wish it were true. We are fed up with kings and emperors, revolutions and changes of governments!
For ages all that came from men was disappointing. We really need the mercy of God.
All the prophets wrote about the coming Messiah and by what signs we could recognize Him! The blind would see and the lame walk!
Come, all to Me who are weary and tired and I shall give you rest! Learn from Me. I am gentle and humble in heart.
I can walk again! Praise God!
Jesus touched my eyes and now I see!
The people with contagious diseases have to live in isolation. They are waiting for Jesus at the city gate.
I hear the bell of a leper! Let's step aside.

Matthew 4: 23-25

Jesus went throughout Galilee, teaching in their synagogues, preaching the good news of the kingdom, and healing every disease and sickness among the people. News about him spread all over Syria, and people brought to him all who were ill with various diseases, those suffering severe pain, the demon-possessed, those having seizures, and the paralyzed, and he healed them. Large crowds from Galilee, the Decapolis, Jerusalem, Judea and the region across the Jordan followed him.

Luke 5: 12-14

While Jesus was in one of the towns, a man came along who was covered with leprosy. When he saw Jesus, he fell with his face to the ground and begged him, "Lord, if you are willing, you can make me clean."
Jesus reached out his hand and touched the man. "I am willing," he said. "Be clean!" And immediately the leprosy left him.
Then Jesus ordered him, "Don't tell anyone, but go, show yourself to the priest and offer the sacrifices that Moses commanded for your cleansing, as a testimony to them."

Matthew 9: 9-13

As Jesus went on from there, he saw a man named Matthew sitting at the tax collector's booth. "Follow me," he told him, and Matthew got up and followed him. While Jesus was having dinner at Matthew's house, many tax collectors and "sinners" came and ate with him and his disciples. When the Pharisees saw this, they asked his disciples, "Why does your teacher eat with tax collectors and 'sinners'?"
On hearing this, Jesus said, "It is not the healthy who need a doctor, but the sick. 13But go and learn what this means: 'I desire mercy, not sacrifice.' For I have not come to call the righteous, but sinners."

One of the following evenings....
Jesus, look, some of these Pharisees are spying. They say that it's really shocking what you do.
Indeed!
A fine prophet, he is!
Look at Him! He feasts with these corrupt custom officers and the worst scum of the town!
You understand nothing. It's not the healthy who need a doctor, but the sick! Rather; think about what is written: God speaks....
.."I desire mercy, not sacrifice!" He loves a man who is compassionate and merciful!
One day the inhabitants of Capernaum gather in the house of Simon, where Jesus is. Everyone wants to hear Him....
Let's go and find out who Jesus is. We'll follow Him discreetly.
But we should hurry if we want to be in the house.
You see? The door is blocked by people. And we cannot get in.
Please, do something! Even though it seems impossible, I have to see Jesus! Only He can heal me!

Mark 2: 1-12

A few days later, when Jesus again entered Capernaum, the people heard that he had come home. So many gathered that there was no room left, not even outside the door, and he preached the word to them. Some men came, bringing to him a paralytic, carried by four of them. Since they could not get him to Jesus because of the crowd, they made an opening in

the roof above Jesus and, after digging through it, lowered the mat the paralyzed man was lying on. When Jesus saw their faith, he said to the paralytic, "Son, your sins are forgiven." Now some teachers of the law were sitting there, thinking to themselves, "Why does this fellow talk like that? He's blaspheming! Who can forgive sins but God alone?" Immediately Jesus knew in his spirit that this was what they were thinking in their hearts, and he said to them, "Why are

What has his paralysis to do with his sins?
Jesus knows that his soul is worse than his body...
Do you hear what He says? That's blasphemy!
Who can forgive sins but God alone?
I know what you are thinking. Tell me: Which is easier, to say to this man: your sins are forgiven....
Or to say: get up and walk home?
I don't have an answer, but I know for sure that both things are very difficult and really need the power of God.
It's better to be silent and I'll wait and see.
You all will witness that the Son of man has authority to forgive sins! This paralytic will be the proof!
Get up! Take up your mat and go home!
Glory and thanks to God!
Astonishing! Son of man He calls himself. Don't forget it! What's He hiding from us?
In His visions the prophet Daniel spoke of One like the Son of man who is God and man but at the same time! I really wonder.

ou thinking these things? Which is easier: to say to the aralytic, 'Your sins are forgiven,' or to say, 'Get up, ake your mat and walk'? But that you may know that he Son of Man has authority on earth to forgive sins . . " He said to the paralytic, "I tell you, get up, take your nat and go home." He got up, took his mat and walked ut in full view of them all. This amazed everyone and hey praised God, saying, "We have never seen any-hing like this!"

Luke 7: 36-50

Now one of the Pharisees invited Jesus to have dinner with him, so he went to the Pharisee's house and reclined at the table. When a woman who had lived a sinful life in that town learned that Jesus was eating at the Pharisee's house, she brought an alabaster jar of perfume, and as she stood behind him at his feet weeping, she began to wet his feet with her tears. Then she wiped

them with her hair, kissed them and poured perfume on them. When the Pharisee who had invited him saw this, he said to himself, "If this man were a prophet, he would know who is touching him and what kind of woman she is--that she is a sinner."
Jesus answered him, "Simon, I have something to tell you."
"Tell me, teacher," he said.
"Two men owed money to a certain moneylender. One owed him five hundred denarii, and the other fifty. Neither of them had the money to pay him back, so he canceled the debts of both. Now which of them will love him more?"

Simon replied, "I suppose the one who had the bigger debt canceled."
"You have judged correctly," Jesus said.
Then he turned toward the woman and said to Simon, "Do you see this woman? I came into your house. You did not give me any water for my feet, but she wet my feet with her tears and wiped them with her hair. You did not give me a kiss, but this woman, from the time I entered, has not stopped kissing my feet. You did not put oil on my head, but she has poured perfume on my feet. Therefore, I tell you, her many sins have been forgiven--for she loved much. But he who has been forgiven little loves little."
Then Jesus said to her, "Your sins are forgiven."
The other guests began to say among themselves, "Who is this who even forgives sins?"
Jesus said to the woman, "Your faith has saved you; go in peace."

Luke 7: 11-17

Soon afterward, Jesus went to a town called Nain, and his disciples and a large crowd went along with him. As he approached the town gate, a dead person was being carried out--the only son of his mother, and she was a widow. And a large crowd from the town was with her. When the Lord saw her, his heart went out to her and he said, "Don't cry."

Then he went up and touched the coffin, and those carrying it stood still. He said, "Young man, I say to you, get up!" The dead man sat up and began to talk, and Jesus gave him back to his mother.

They were all filled with awe and praised God. "A great prophet has appeared among us," they said. "God has come to help his people." This news about Jesus spread throughout Judea and the surrounding country.

John 6: 1-15

Some time after this, Jesus crossed to the far shore of the Sea of Galilee (that is, the Sea of Tiberias), and a great crowd of people followed him because they saw the miraculous signs he had performed on the sick. Then Jesus went up on a mountainside and sat down with his disciples. The Jewish Passover Feast was near.

When Jesus looked up and saw a great crowd coming toward him, he said to Philip, "Where shall we buy bread for these people to eat?" He asked this only to test him, for he already had in mind what he was going to do.

Philip answered him, "Eight months' wages would not buy enough bread for each one to have a bite!" Another of his disciples, Andrew, Simon Peter's brother, spoke up, "Here is a boy with five small barley loaves and two small fish, but how far will they go among so many?"

Jesus said, "Have the people sit down." There was plenty of grass in that place, and the men sat down, about five thousand of them. Jesus then took the loaves, gave thanks, and distributed to those who were seated as much as they wanted. He did the same with the fish.

When they had all had enough to eat, he said to his

After everybody has eaten enough...
Gather the left-overs, don't waste anything.
Ten...eleven...twelve baskets full of bread.
Meanwhile, some are discussing the event...
Enormous, what this Jesus has done! Enough food for so many with so little at first!
That reminds me of the prophet Elijah in his days.
Yes, our holy books inform us that one day he fed a hundred persons with only two loaves and also had left-overs like we
had today. Could Jesus be the new prophet?
Sure! He must be the long awaited Messiah!
Pass the word around; we want Jesus to be our king.
Let's gather around our king.
We form an army...with him as our leader and we drive the Romans away.
But Jesus recognized that they intended to make him their king by force...
I shall escape, they are beside themselves... misunderstood my message....dreaming
about a fighting Messiah... as the night approaches I shall go into the mountains!
Some time afterwards, Jesus leads His disciples to the north of the region of Caesarea (nowadays called the Golan Heights) near Mount Hermon.

isciples, "Gather the pieces that are left over. Let noth-
ng be wasted." So they gathered them and filled twelve
askets with the pieces of the five barley loaves left
ver by those who had eaten.
After the people saw the miraculous sign that Jesus did,
hey began to say, "Surely this is the Prophet who is to
ome into the world." Jesus, knowing that they intended
o come and make him king by force, withdrew again to
mountain by himself.

Matthew 16: 13-17

When Jesus came to the region of Caesarea Philippi, he asked his disciples, "Who do people say the Son of Man is?"

They replied, "Some say John the Baptist; others say Elijah; and still others, Jeremiah or one of the prophets."

"But what about you?" he asked. "Who do you s ay I am?"

Simon Peter answered, "You are the Christ, the Son of the living God."

Jesus replied, "Blessed are you, Simon son of Jonah, for this was not revealed to you by man, but by my Father in heaven.

Matthew 20: 20-24
Then the mother of Zebedee's sons came to Jesus with her sons and, kneeling down, asked a favor of him.
"What is it you want?" he asked.
She said, "Grant that one of these two sons of mine may sit at your right and the other at your left in your kingdom."
"You don't know what you are asking," Jesus said to them. "Can you drink the cup I am going to drink?"
"We can," they answered.

Jesus said to them, "You will indeed drink from my cup, but to sit at my right or left is not for me to grant. These places belong to those for whom they have been prepared by my Father."
When the ten heard about this, they were indignant with the two brothers.

Matthew 16: 21-23
From that time on Jesus began to explain to his disciples that he must go to Jerusalem and suffer many things at the hands of the elders, chief priests and teachers of the law, and that he must be killed and on the third day be raised to life.
Peter took him aside and began to rebuke him. "Never, Lord!" he said. "This shall never happen to you!"
Jesus turned and said to Peter, "Get behind me, Satan! You are a stumbling block to me; you do not have in mind the things of God, but the things of men."

Matthew 4: 1-11
Then Jesus was led by the Spirit into the desert to be tempted by the devil. After fasting forty days and forty nights, he was hungry. The tempter came to him and said, "If you are the Son of God, tell these stones to become bread."
Jesus answered, "It is written: 'Man does not live on bread alone, but on every word that comes from the

"You're hungry," he whispered, "but if you are the Son of God, tell these stones to become bread"...I refused his temptation of being a Messiah, a Christ who would not suffer-be it suffering from hunger... Man does not live by bread alone, but by every word that comes from God!
I declined his temptation of being a Messiah, a Christ, who would win the people by means of sensational appearances.
other time I was on the ghest peak of the mple."Throw yourself down," e Devil whispered,"no harm ll touch you. If you are the n of God, He'll protect you d the people will adore you."

nouth of God.'"
'hen the devil took him to the holy city and had him tand on the highest point of the temple. "If you are the on of God," he said, "throw yourself down. For it is vritten: " 'He will command his angels concerning you, nd they will lift you up in their hands, so that you will ot strike your foot against a stone.' "
esus answered him, "It is also written: 'Do not put the ord your God to the test.' "

After that I stood on a very high mountain... "Look at all the kingdoms of the world and their splendour," the Devil whispered again. "All this I will give you when you will bow down and worship me." I answered:
"Away from me, Satan! It is written: Worship the Lord, your God and serve only Him!"
Friends, don't fall for these temptations. I am God's servant of whom the prophet Isaiah announced:..."I shall give my life for my people!"
What a disappointing speech! I'm losing my time and chance with Jesus. I should have realized that before!
I'm confused. I don't understand it anymore....
My friends, prepare a camp at the foot of this mountain.
And you, Peter, James and John, come with Me! We'll spend the night together on the mountain.

Again, the devil took him to a very high mountain and showed him all the kingdoms of the world and their splendor. "All this I will give you," he said, "if you will bow down and worship me."
Jesus said to him, "Away from me, Satan! For it is written: 'Worship the Lord your God, and serve him only.'" Then the devil left him, and angels came and attended him.

I've taken you three apart to comfort you tonight.
On a mountain Moses as well as Elijah met with God and took courage.

At midnight, a blinding light awakes Peter, James and John. Jesus appears in brilliant light to them and is talking with Moses and Elijah.

/hen the appearance ends, ıppearance ends, :hey see Jesus ust as before.

At daybreak, the four men pack and go down the mountain.

Matthew 17: 1-9

After six days Jesus took with him Peter, James and John the brother of James, and led them up a high mountain by themselves. There he was transfigured before them. His face shone like the sun, and his clothes became as white as the light. Just then there appeared before them Moses and Elijah, talking with Jesus.

Peter said to Jesus, "Lord, it is good for us to be here. If you wish, I will put up three shelters--one for you, one for Moses and one for Elijah."

While he was still speaking, a bright cloud enveloped them, and a voice from the cloud said, "This is my Son, whom I love; with him I am well pleased. Listen to him!"

When the disciples heard this, they fell facedown to the ground, terrified. But Jesus came and touched them. "Get up," he said. "Don't be afraid." When they looked up, they saw no one except Jesus.

As they were coming down the mountain, Jesus instructed them, "Don't tell anyone what you have seen, until the Son of Man has been raised from the dead."

There are no words to express the events of last night... it's become very clear to me that Jesus is far greater than Moses and Elijah!
Oh, yes. They have only prepared His coming... He is part of God's glory Himself!
I heard the voice from heaven saying: "Jesus is My Son Whom I love... follow Him, listen to Him."
I saw the same, John, and I tell you that Jesus is the Messiah, the Christ. Surely, He's the Son of the living God!
Peter, I heard you saying: "Lord, it is good for us to be here. If You wish, I will put up three shelters; one for You, one for Moses and one for Elijah..."
My friends, I command you: don't tell anyone what you have seen...until the Son of man has been raised from the dead!
I don't fully understand, but we promise to remain silent.
Come along, friends, let's go up to Jerusalem!
James, John and I, Peter, trust that God is with us.

Jesus has decided to go up to Jerusalem for the Pass-over Feast...with His disciples He comes to the Mount of Olives.
Here they meet some pilgrims from Galilee, who are also going to Jerusalem...
Look! There's Jesus of Nazareth!
The famous prophet of our province of Galilee!
We must organize a parade when Jesus enters the city!
People of Galilee, let's gather around Him... we'll cheer Him on
as the Messiah! That will be a real sensation!
Jesus, please for once accept this proposal!
I agree...
Go into that village where you'll find a colt. Untie her and bring her to Me... I will ride on her...

Matthew 21: 1-17

As they approached Jerusalem and came to Bethphage on the Mount of Olives, Jesus sent two disciples, saying to them, "Go to the village ahead of you, and at once you will find a donkey tied there, with her colt by her. Untie them and bring them to me. If anyone says anything to you, tell him that the Lord needs them, and he will send them right away."

This took place to fulfill what was spoken through the prophet: "Say to the Daughter of Zion, 'See, your king comes to you, gentle and riding on a donkey, on a colt, the foal of a donkey.' "

The disciples went and did as Jesus had instructed them.

They brought the donkey and the colt, placed their cloaks on them, and Jesus sat on them. A very large crowd spread their cloaks on the road, while others cut branches from the trees and spread them on the road. The crowds that went ahead of him and those that followed shouted, "Hosanna to the Son of David!" "Blessed is he who comes in the name of the Lord!" "Hosanna in the highest!"
When Jesus entered Jerusalem, the whole city was stirred and asked, "Who is this?"
The crowds answered, "This is Jesus, the prophet from Nazareth in Galilee."
Jesus entered the temple area and drove out all who were buying and selling there. He overturned the

To whom are you cheering?
Jesus of Nazareth, the new prophet!
What does this mean?
Mm...when the Romans find out about this, their army might very well take action...
he parade has arrived at the emple area...beggars, sick and isabled people follow Him...
Get away, you dirty people! You're unclean and are not allowed to enter the Temple!
Never mind that I'm disabled; Jesus will heal me!
Now the children start cheering Jesus.
Long live Jesus of Nazareth!
Be quiet, this is the holy Temple!

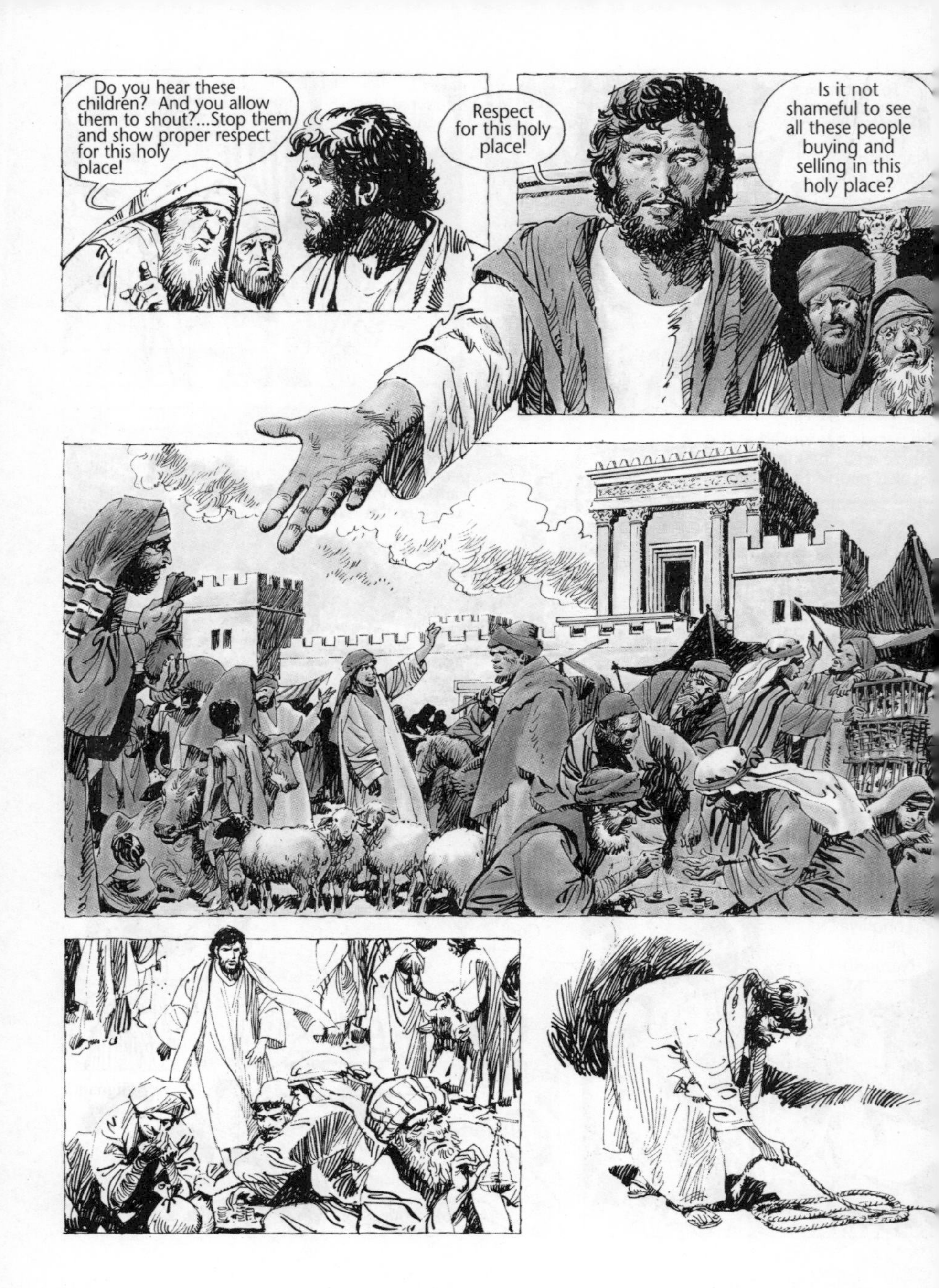
Do you hear these children? And you allow them to shout?...Stop them and show proper respect for this holy place!
Respect for this holy place!
Is it not shameful to see all these people buying and selling in this holy place?

tables of the money changers and the benches of those selling doves. "It is written," he said to them, " 'My house will be called a house of prayer,' but you are making it a 'den of robbers.'"
The blind and the lame came to him at the temple, and he healed them. But when the chief priests and the teachers of the law saw the wonderful things he did and the children shouting in the temple area, "Hosanna to the Son of David," they were indignant. "Do you hear what these children are saying?" they asked him.
"Yes," replied Jesus, "have you never read, " 'From the lips of children and infants you have ordained praise'?" And he left them and went out of the city to Bethany, where he spent the night.

It was a parable indeed. Jesus spoke of His body, the new temple of God!...Destroyed, killed, He would rise again from the dead after three days.
After Jesus' resurrection the disciples understood it.

John 11: 47-50

Then the chief priests and the Pharisees called a meeting of the Sanhedrin.
"What are we accomplishing?" they asked. "Here is this man performing many miraculous signs. If we let him go on like this, everyone will believe in him, and then the Romans will come and take away both our place and our nation."
Then one of them, named Caiaphas, who was high priest that year, spoke up, "You know nothing at all! You do not realize that it is better for you that one man die for the people than that the whole nation perish."

Matthew 26: 3-5, 14-16

Then the chief priests and the elders of the people assembled in the palace of the high priest, whose name was Caiaphas, and they plotted to arrest Jesus in some sly way and kill him. "But not during the Feast," they said, "or there may be a riot among the people."...

Then one of the Twelve--the one called Judas Iscariot--went to the chief priests and asked, "What are you willing to give me if I hand him over to you?" So they counted out for him thirty silver coins. From then on Judas watched for an opportunity to hand him over.

For some weeks Jesus and His disciples were in hiding, while the servants of the high priest were searching for Him...
My friends, today the Pass-over is celebrated. Peter and John, go and make preparations for us to eat the Pass-over.
Yes, Lord. But where? With whom?
I've reserved a large room in Jerusalem. You must go and find it....
..As you enter the city, you'll meet a man carrying a jar of water. Follow him to the house he enters. That will be the place.
Aha, Jesus doesn't trust me anymore...but as the treasurer I have the right to prepare the Pass-over ...then I would've known the meeting place!
Then I could have informed the authorities so that they could have arrested Him.
Some hours later...
Women carrying water jars, that's nothing special.
But there I see a man carrying a jar, which is unusual! Could he be the man?
It must be! Let's follow him!

Luke 22: 7-12

Then came the day of Unleavened Bread on which the Passover lamb had to be sacrificed. Jesus sent Peter and John, saying, "Go and make preparations for us to eat the Passover."

"Where do you want us to prepare for it?" they asked.

He replied, "As you enter the city, a man carrying a jar of water will meet you. Follow him to the house that he enters, and say to the owner of the house, 'The Teacher asks: Where is the guest room, where I may eat the Passover with my disciples?' He will show you a large upper room, all furnished. Make preparations there."

They recline at the table, but a dispute arises...
Leave this place to me, I have the right to be next to Jesus!
Never! I'm here and I'll stay here! Are we not all in the same group?
Yes, that's right! No favoring! No special privileges!
My friends, wait a moment! Before you take your places...
You know that the kings of the Gentiles lord it over them, they rule over their people with force and the sword, but you should not act like that....
..instead, your duty is to serve one another.
After that...
Look what He's doing!
I don't understand! It looks like he's getting ready to do some cleaning

John 13: 2-11, 21-30

The evening meal was being served, and the devil had already prompted Judas Iscariot, son of Simon, to betray Jesus. Jesus knew that the Father had put all things under his power, and that he had come from God and was returning to God; so he got up from the meal, took off his outer clothing, and wrapped a towel around his waist. After that, he poured water into a basin and began to wash his disciples' feet, drying them with the towel that was wrapped around him.

He came to Simon Peter, who said to him, "Lord, are you going to wash my feet?"

Jesus replied, "You do not realize now what I am doing, but later you will understand."

"No," said Peter, "you shall never wash my feet."

Jesus answered, "Unless I wash you, you have no part with me."

"Then, Lord," Simon Peter replied, "not just my fee but my hands and my head as well!"

At the beginning of the meal, Jesus and the disciples eat the bitter salad, to remember the time of oppression which their forefathers experienced in Egypt before the great Exodus.
My friends, I have something sad to tell you. One of you is going to betray Me.
Yes, I mean it. One of you, eating at My table...
What? Is this possible? That would be horrible!
Who of us could do that?
I hope you don't mean me?
..or me?
Simon Peter motioned to John and said: Ask Him who He means... we could try and prevent it.

Jesus answered, "A person who has had a bath needs only to wash his feet; his whole body is clean. And you are clean, though not every one of you." For he knew who was going to betray him, and that was why he said not every one was clean...
After he had said this, Jesus was troubled in spirit and testified, "I tell you the truth, one of you is going to betray me."
His disciples stared at one another, at a loss to know which of them he meant. One of them, the disciple

whom Jesus loved, was reclining next to him. Simon Peter motioned to this disciple and said, "Ask him which one he means."
Leaning back against Jesus, he asked him, "Lord, who is it?"
Jesus answered, "It is the one to whom I will give this piece of bread when I have dipped it in the dish."

Then, dipping the piece of bread, he gave it to Judas Iscariot, son of Simon. As soon as Judas took the bread, Satan entered into him.
"What you are about to do, do quickly," Jesus told him, but no one at the meal understood why Jesus said this to him. Since Judas had charge of the money, some thought Jesus was telling him to buy what was needed for the Feast, or to give something to the poor. As soon as Judas had taken the bread, he went out. And it was night.

Luke 22: 19-20

And he took bread, gave thanks and broke it, and ave it to them, saying, "This is my body given for ou; do this in remembrance of me."

In the same way, after the supper he took the cup, saying, "This cup is the new covenant in my blood, which is poured out for you.

After eating the bread, Jesus takes the cup and gives thanks...
Then Jesus and His disciples end the meal and sing the songs of Pass-over.

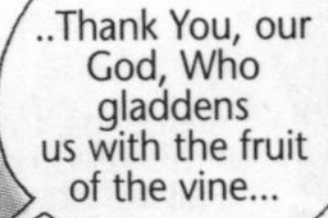

..Thank You, our God, Who gladdens us with the fruit of the vine...

..but He adds...

..Take this cup of the New Covenant in My blood, which is poured out for many for the forgiveness of their sins.

Do this in rememberance of Me.

Mark 14: 26-72
When they had sung a hymn, they went out to the Mount of Olives.
"You will all fall away," Jesus told them, "for it is written: " 'I will strike the shepherd, and the sheep will be scattered.' But after I have risen, I will go ahead of you into Galilee."
Peter declared, "Even if all fall away, I will not."

After that they leave Jerusalem...

Where's he taking us?

Mark 14: 26-72

When they had sung a hymn, they went out to the Mount of Olives.

"You will all fall away," Jesus told them, "for it is written: " 'I will strike the shepherd, and the sheep will be scattered.' But after I have risen, I will go ahead of you into Galilee."

Peter declared, "Even if all fall away, I will not."

"I tell you the truth," Jesus answered, "today--yes, tonight--before the rooster crows twice you yourself will disown me three times."

But Peter insisted emphatically, "Even if I have to die with you, I will never disown you." And all the

Jesus took the three disciples along with Him....

Dear friends, I'm overwhelmed with sorrow to the point of death!

Stay alert and keep watch with me. I'll go and pray over there...

Jesus returns to His disciples to find comfort, but...

Abba, Father! Everything is possible with You. Let me escape from the terrible events that will come over Me...
...yet not my will, but Your will be done!

...Simon, are you asleep? Could you not keep watch for one hour?

others said the same.
They went to a place called Gethsemane, and Jesus said to his disciples, "Sit here while I pray." He took Peter, James and John along with him, and he began to be deeply distressed and troubled. "My soul is overwhelmed with sorrow to the point of death," he said to them. "Stay here and keep watch."
Going a little farther, he fell to the ground and prayed that if possible the hour might pass from him. "Abba, Father," he said, "everything is possible for you. Take this cup from me. Yet not what I will, but what you will."
Then he returned to his disciples and found them sleeping. "Simon," he said to Peter, "are you asleep? Could you not keep watch for one hour? Watch and

What matters now is to watch and pray so that you will not fall into temptation....
.you see, the spirit is willing, but the body is weak.
Meanwhile...at the garden entrance ...
Judas, it is very dark under the trees. What does He look like, this Jesus? Whom should we arrest?
The man whom I'll kiss, He'll be your man!
My hour has come! Look, I am betrayed into the hands of sinners! Rise! Let's go! Here comes my betrayer.
Good evening, Master!

pray so that you will not fall into temptation. The spirit is willing, but the body is weak."
Once more he went away and prayed the same thing. When he came back, he again found them sleeping, because their eyes were heavy. They did not know what to say to him.
Returning the third time, he said to them, "Are you still sleeping and resting? Enough! The hour has come. Look, the Son of Man is betrayed into the hands of sinners. Rise! Let us go! Here comes my betrayer!"
Just as he was speaking, Judas, one of the Twelve, appeared. With him was a crowd armed with swords and clubs, sent from the chief priests, the teachers of the law, and the elders.

Now the betrayer had arranged a signal with them: "The one I kiss is the man; arrest him and lead him away under guard." Going at once to Jesus, Judas

After the first surprise, the disciples of Jesus recovered themselves...
So you come secretly, at night to arrest us! I'll teach you!
And you'll remember this for the rest of your life!
AUGH!
Peter, put your sword away!
..for all who use the sword, will die by the sword!
Am I leading a rebellion, that you come out with swords and clubs to capture me?
Every day I was in the Temple courts teaching....You did not arrest me there.... But this is your hour... when darkness reigns.
Jesus allows them to seize him...seeing this, all the disciples desert Him and flee away.

said, "Rabbi!" and kissed him. The men seized Jesus and arrested him. Then one of those standing near drew his sword and struck the servant of the high priest, cutting off his ear.
"Am I leading a rebellion," said Jesus, "that you have come out with swords and clubs to capture me? Every day I was with you, teaching in the temple courts, and you did not arrest me. But the Scriptures must be fulfilled." Then everyone deserted him and fled.
A young man, wearing nothing but a linen garment, was following Jesus. When they seized him, he fled naked, leaving his garment behind.
They took Jesus to the high priest, and all the chief priests, elders and teachers of the law came togethe

Peter followed him at a distance, right into the courtyard of the high priest. There he sat with the guards and warmed himself at the fire.
The chief priests and the whole Sanhedrin were looking for evidence against Jesus so that they could put him to death, but they did not find any. Many testified falsely against him, but their statements did not agree.

I don't trust that newcomer....
...he was also with that Jesus...?...
?

Who are you talking about? Jesus of Nazareth? I don't know Him!
Listen to me! I'm telling you....
...that I don't know that man!

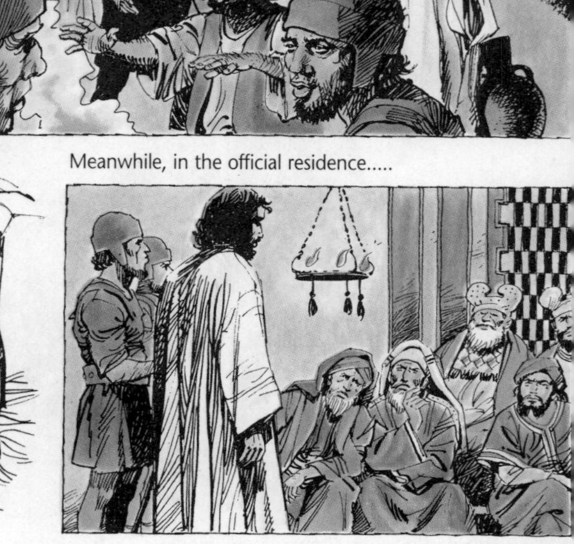
I just passed by...it is rather cold tonight, so I came in to warm myself.
Really? But you act suspicious. You are one of His disciples
Meanwhile, in the official residence.....

Jesus is taken to the high priest, who has called a meeting of the Sanhedrin: the priests, the elders and teachers of the law...
I've called you to investigate the case of Jesus of Nazareth, because the highest interest of our nation is at stake!
His sensational actions are disturbing public order, his revolutionary statements against the Temple and our religion have caused me to arrest Him...
...and bring him before our court so that we can try him according to our laws. Bring in the witnesses!
I heard him say: "you may destroy this Temple and in three days I will rebuild it!"
No, He didn't say that! But rather, "I'll destroy this man-made temple and I'll build another one, not made by man!"
It's hard to believe that he dared to
speak against the glory of God and the Temple.
I record: the witnesses don't agree. Jesus doesn't answer anything...the assembly is divided and confused.

Then some stood up and gave this false testimony against him: "We heard him say, 'I will destroy this man-made temple and in three days will build another, not made by man.' " Yet even then their testimony did not agree.
Then the high priest stood up before them and asked Jesus, "Are you not going to answer? What is this testimony that these men are bringing against you?" But Jesus remained silent and gave no answer.
Again the high priest asked him, "Are you the Christ, the Son of the Blessed One?"

"I am," said Jesus. "And you will see the Son of Man sitting at the right hand of the Mighty One and coming on the clouds of heaven."
The high priest tore his clothes. "Why do we need any more witnesses?" he asked. "You have heard the blasphemy. What do you think?"
They all condemned him as worthy of death. Then some began to spit at him; they blindfolded him, struck him with their fists, and said, "Prophesy!" And the guards took him and beat him.
While Peter was below in the courtyard, one of the ser-

vant girls of the high priest came by. When she saw Peter warming himself, she looked closely at him. "You also were with that Nazarene, Jesus," she said. But he denied it. "I don't know or understand what you're talking about," he said, and went out into the entryway.
When the servant girl saw him there, she said again to those standing around, "This fellow is one of them." Again he denied it.
After a little while, those standing near said to Peter, "Surely you are one of them, for you are a Galilean." He began to call down curses on himself, and he swore to them, "I don't know this man you're talking about."
Immediately the rooster crowed the second time. Then Peter remembered the word Jesus had spoken to him: "Before the rooster crows twice you will disown me three times." And he broke down and wept.

Judas heard that the Sanhedrin has condemned Jesus.
He is filled with remorse and hurries to the Sanhedrin to return the thirty silver coins....
Woe to me! I've sinned! I,ve betrayed innocent blood!
I don't want your money!
I,ve betrayed an innocent man!
That's your business, not ours!
In great despair Judas leaves and hangs himself.
The next morning, Jesus is taken to Pilate...

Matthew 27: 3-5

When Judas, who had betrayed him, saw that Jesus was condemned, he was seized with remorse and returned the thirty silver coins to the chief priests and the elders. "I have sinned," he said, "for I have betrayed innocent blood."
"What is that to us?" they replied. "That's your responsibility."
So Judas threw the money into the temple and left. Then he went away and hanged himself.

John 18: 28-19:16

Then the Jews led Jesus from Caiaphas to the palace of the Roman governor. By now it was early morning, and to avoid ceremonial uncleanness the Jews did not enter the palace; they wanted to be able to eat the Passover. So Pilate came out to them and asked, "What charges are you bringing against this man?"
"If he were not a criminal," they replied, "we would not have handed him over to you."
Pilate said, "Take him yourselves and judge him by your own law."
"But we have no right to execute anyone," the Jews objected. This happened so that the words Jesus had spoken indicating the kind of death he was going to die would be fulfilled.
Pilate then went back inside the palace, summoned Jesus and asked him, "Are you the king of the Jews?"
"Is that your own idea," Jesus asked, "or did others talk to you about me?"
"Am I a Jew?" Pilate replied. "It was your people and your chief priests who handed you over to me. What is it you have done?"
Jesus said, "My kingdom is not of this world. If it

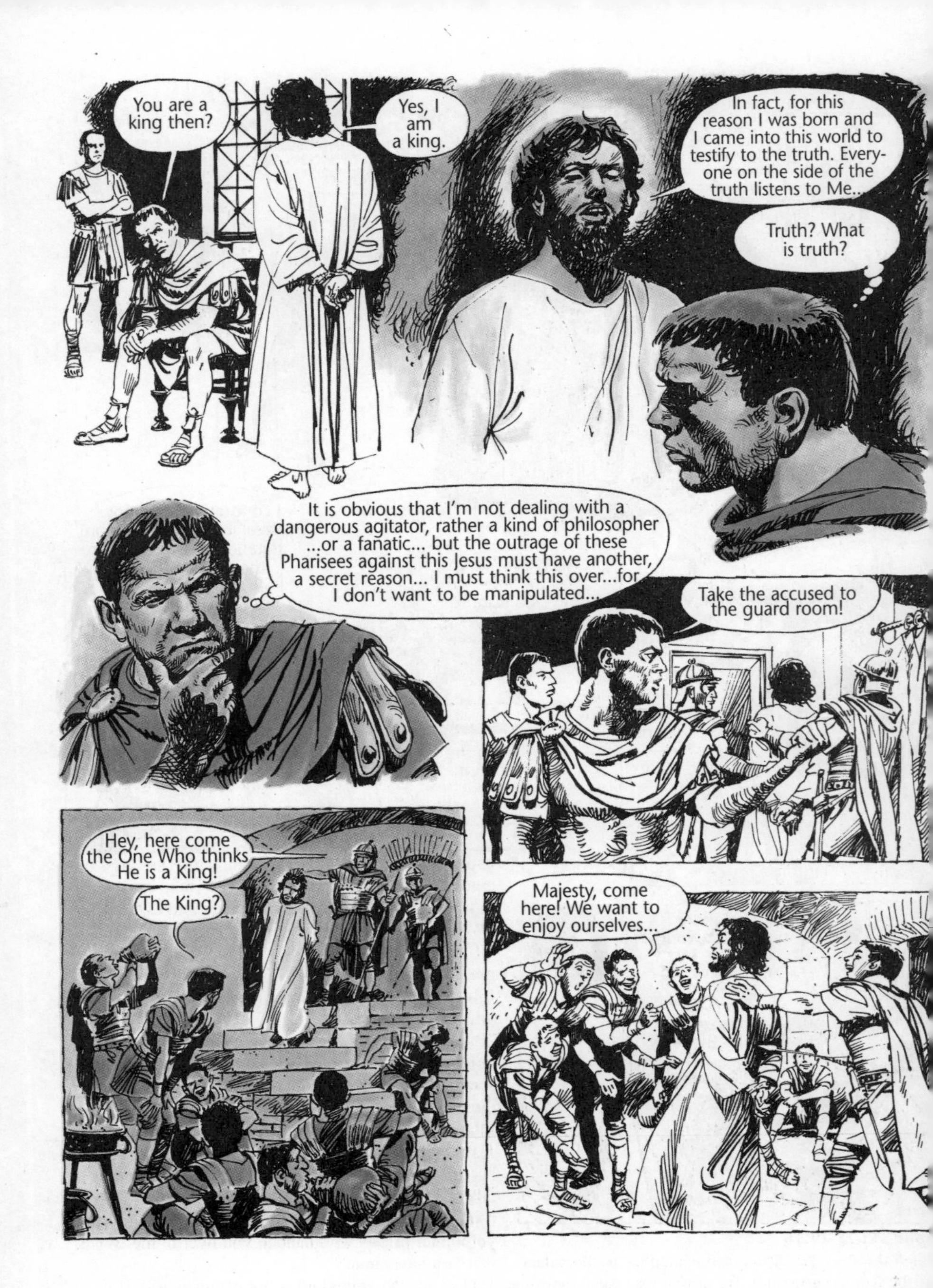
You are a king then?
Yes, I am a king.
In fact, for this reason I was born and I came into this world to testify to the truth. Every-one on the side of the truth listens to Me...
Truth? What is truth?
It is obvious that I'm not dealing with a dangerous agitator, rather a kind of philosopher ...or a fanatic... but the outrage of these Pharisees against this Jesus must have another, a secret reason... I must think this over...for I don't want to be manipulated...
Take the accused to the guard room!
Hey, here come the One Who thinks He is a King!
The King?
Majesty, come here! We want to enjoy ourselves...

, my servants would fight to prevent my arrest by ews. But now my kingdom is from another place." are a king, then!" said Pilate.

Jesus answered, "You are right in saying I am a king. In fact, for this reason I was born, and for this I came into the world, to testify to the truth. Everyone on the side of truth listens to me."
"What is truth?" Pilate asked. With this he went out again to the Jews and said, "I find no basis for a charge against him. But it is your custom for me to release to you one prisoner at the time of the Passover. Do you want me to release 'the king of the Jews'?"
They shouted back, "No, not him! Give us Barabbas!" Now Barabbas had taken part in a rebellion.
Then Pilate took Jesus and had him flogged. The soldiers twisted together a crown of thorns and put it on his head. They clothed him in a purple robe and went up to him again and again, saying, "Hail, king of the Jews!" And they struck him in the face.

Tomorrow will be the great Sabbath-Day (Pass-over), the most sacred national Feast of the Jews...
..and now the court yard is filling up with people who want to see you ....
..and expect you to release a prisoner of their choice.
I know, and I have an idea.
We all agree that we want Barabbas freed!
Agreed! Barabbas!
A real rebel and who isn't afraid to use terrorist tactics to overthrow the Romans.
Citizens of Jerusalem! Please be calm. We want you to celebrate your Pass-over in peace and trust that all pilgrims will be received well.
We, the Zealots, need a man like Barabbas!

I remind you, that the Roman army has been strengthened and is watching from the Citadel Antonia to prevent any problems.
Finally, according to the custom at the time of Pass-over, I'll release a prisoner of your choice.
Two of them are well known: Jesus and Barabbas. Which one of them do you want released?
Give us Barabbas!
Long live Barabbas! Set Barabbas free!
Did I hear him speaking of Jesus of Nazareth, the great prophet? Did the Romans arrest him?
When? and for what reasons?
Apparently the people are not informed ...otherwise they would come and demonstrate in favour of Jesus.
I see mostly Zealots and foreigners. How sad!
What a strange people! They prefer a rebel over a wise and innocent man!
And I thought that I could cross the plans of these Pharisees!

Silence! I'll have the two prisoners brought out, then you can see them and make a better choice.
Guards! Bring Jesus and Barabbas here!
Look the man!
No, not Jesus, but Barabbas!
Barabbas! We want Barabbas! Set him free!
Crucify! Crucify Jesus! He deserves death!
Yes, call for Barabbas! you'll do the nation a great service!
Jesus is a tempter! He deceives the people! He deserves death!
Barab-bas!!
Barab-bas!!
Aren't you ashamed to have Jesus of Nazareth put to death?
A prophet who heals the sick, blind and paralyzed...and gives hope to the poor, exploited and desperate people?

Once more Pilate came out and said to the Jews, "Look, I am bringing him out to you to let you know that I find no basis for a charge against him." When Jesus came out wearing the crown of thorns and the purple robe, Pilate said to them, "Here is the man!" As soon as the chief priests and their officials saw him, they shouted, "Crucify! Crucify!"
But Pilate answered, "You take him and crucify him. As for me, I find no basis for a charge against him."
The Jews insisted, "We have a law, and according to that law he must die, because he claimed to be the Son of God."
When Pilate heard this, he was even more afraid, and he went back inside the palace. "Where do you come from?" he asked Jesus, but Jesus gave him no answer. "Do you refuse to speak to me?" Pilate said. "Don't you realize I have power either to free you or to crucify you?"

Jesus answered, "You would have no power over me if it were not given to you from above. Therefore the one who handed me over to you is guilty of a greater sin."

From then on, Pilate tried to set Jesus free, but the Jews kept shouting, "If you let this man go, you are no friend of Caesar. Anyone who claims to be a king opposes Caesar."
When Pilate heard this, he brought Jesus out and sat down on the judge's seat at a place known as the Stone Pavement (which in Aramaic is Gabbatha). It was the day of Preparation of Passover Week, about the sixth hour.
"Here is your king," Pilate said to the Jews.
But they shouted, "Take him away! Take him away! Crucify him!"
"Shall I crtcify your king?" Pilate asked.

"We have no king but Caesar," the chief priests answered.
Finally Pilate handed him over to them to be crucified.

Here's the substitute for Barabbas.
Don't worry! We'll take care of Him.
He pretends to be a king, so give Him a real good treatment! Royally!
On this day three executions will take place...and according to custom, every condemned man must be whipped.
That's it for the King of the Jews.... I think He's had enough.
Now Jesus must carry the cross-beam of his own cross, with a notice around his neck, proclaiming the judgement.

And the sad procession starts moving....
IESVS NAZARENVS
REX IVDAEORVM
Make room! Let us pass!
Who's that one?
He looks like Jesus of Nazareth...the famous prophet!

Here we see the man, who only did good; he healed the sick and defended the poor and the oppressed. Oh, what a terrible injustice!
Woe to them! In their hatred they handed Him over to the Romans.
The Pharisees hated Him, because He spoke the truth and exposed their hypocrisy!
One is falling down!
He is too weak to carry his cross; he lost too much blood because of the whipping.
Hey, you! I order you to carry the cross of this condemned man to Golgotha! That is an order! Now, obey!
Me?....But I'm not from Jerusalem! I'm a decent man from Cyrene!
Be wise and don't resist or you will be sorry. Romans are tough and besides, it's not so far to Golgotha from here.
I'll carry it for you! Get up!
Help Him, He's innocent! He's Jesus of Nazareth, the great prophet!

Daughters of Jerusalem, why do you weep for me? Rather weep for yourselves and your children...
..as not long from now a terrible punishment will fall on Jerusalem.
Look, here is the place for the execution, which is called Golgotha or "the skull".
From far the rock looks indeed like a skull.
And the place is well chosen! Everyone who comes to Jerusalem is reminded of the cost to challenge the Romans.

Luke 23: 25-56
He released the man who had been thrown into prison for insurrection and murder, the one they asked for, and surrendered Jesus to their will.
As they led him away, they seized Simon from Cyrene, who was on his way in from the country, and put the cross on him and made him carry it behind Jesus. A large number of people followed him, including women who mourned and wailed for him. Jesus turned and said to them, "Daughters of Jerusalem, do not weep for me; weep for yourselves and for your children. For the time will come when you will say, 'Blessed are the barren women, the wombs that never bore and the breasts that never nursed!' Then " 'they will say to the mountains, "Fall on us!" and to the hills, "Cover us!" ' For if men do these things when the tree is green, what will happen

When they arrive at Golgotha, they brutally take off Jesus' clothing.
Pile these clothes up over there! We will divide them later!

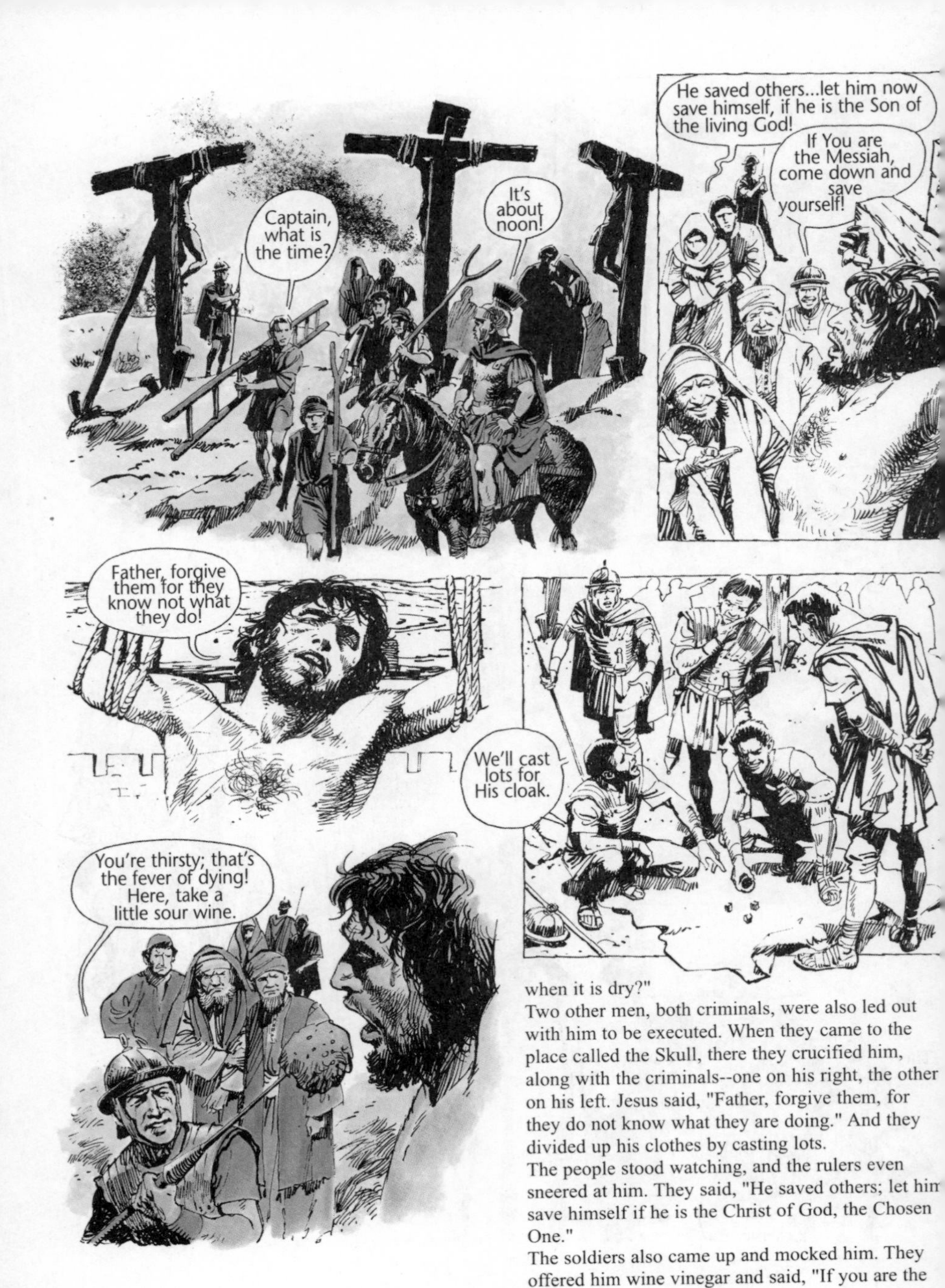

when it is dry?"
Two other men, both criminals, were also led out with him to be executed. When they came to the place called the Skull, there they crucified him, along with the criminals--one on his right, the other on his left. Jesus said, "Father, forgive them, for they do not know what they are doing." And they divided up his clothes by casting lots.
The people stood watching, and the rulers even sneered at him. They said, "He saved others; let him save himself if he is the Christ of God, the Chosen One."
The soldiers also came up and mocked him. They offered him wine vinegar and said, "If you are the king of the Jews, save yourself."

There was a written notice above him, which read:|sc THIS IS THE KING OF THE JEWS.
One of the criminals who hung there hurled insults at him: "Aren't you the Christ? Save yourself and us!"
But the other criminal rebuked him. "Don't you fear God," he said, "since you are under the same sentence? We are punished justly, for we are getting what our deeds deserve. But this man has done nothing wrong."

Then he said, "Jesus, remember me when you come into your kingdom."
Jesus answered him, "I tell you the truth, today you will be with me in paradise."

It was now about the sixth hour, and darkness came over the whole land until the ninth hour, for the sun stopped shining. And the curtain of the temple was torn in two. Jesus called out with a loud voice, "Father, into your hands I commit my spirit." When he had said this, he breathed his last.
The centurion, seeing what had happened, praised God and said, "Surely this was a righteous man." When all the people who had gathered to witness this sight saw what took place, they beat their breasts and went away. But all those who knew him, including the women who had followed him from Galilee, stood at a distance, watching these things.
Now there was a man named Joseph, a member of the Council, a good and upright man, who had not consented to their decision and action. He came from the Judean town of Arimathea and he was waiting for the kingdom of God. Going to Pilate, he asked for Jesus' body. Then he took it down, wrapped it in linen cloth and placed it in a tomb cut in the rock, one in which

no one had yet been laid. It was Preparation Day, and the Sabbath was about to begin.
The women who had come with Jesus from Galilee followed Joseph and saw the tomb and how his body was laid in it. Then they went home and prepared spices and perfumes. But they rested on the Sabbath in obedience to the commandment.

At last the heavy stone is rolled in front
of the entrance of the tomb..

ark 16: 1-7

hen the Sabbath was over, Mary Magdalene, ary the mother of James, and Salome bought ces so that they might go to anoint Jesus' body. ry early on the first day of the week, just after rise, they were on their way to the tomb and y asked each other, "Who will roll the stone ay from the entrance of the tomb?"
t when they looked up, they saw that the stone, ich was very large, had been rolled away. As y entered the tomb, they saw a young man ssed in a white robe sitting on the right side, and y were alarmed.
on't be alarmed," he said. "You are looking for us the Nazarene, who was crucified. He has en! He is not here. See the place where they laid . But go, tell his disciples and Peter, 'He is going ahead of you into Galilee. There you will see him, just as he told you.' "

John 20: 1-15

Early on the first day of the week, while it was still dark, Mary Magdalene went to the tomb and saw that the stone had been removed from the entrance. So she came running to Simon Peter and the other disciple, the one Jesus loved, and said, "They have taken the Lord out of the tomb, and we don't know where they have put him!"

So Peter and the other disciple started for the tomb. Both were running, but the other disciple outran Peter and reached the tomb first. He bent over and looked in at the strips of linen lying there but did not go in. Then Simon Peter, who was behind him, arrived and went into the tomb. He saw the strips of linen lying there, as well as the burial cloth that had been around Jesus' head. The cloth was folded up by itself, separate from the linen. Finally the other dis-

Mary Magdalene has returned to the tomb...wondering and weeping..
Woman, why do you look for the living among the dead?
Why do you cry? What's the matter?
Gardener, if you have carried away His body, tell me where you have laid Him...
Mary!
Lord Jesus?!

ciple, who had reached the tomb first, also went inside. He saw and believed. (They still did not understand from Scripture that Jesus had to rise from the dead.)
Then the disciples went back to their homes, but Mary stood outside the tomb crying. As she wept, she bent over to look into the tomb and saw two angels in white, seated where Jesus' body had been, one at the head and the other at the foot.
They asked her, "Woman, why are you crying?"
"They have taken my Lord away," she said, "and I don't know where they have put him." At this, she turned around and saw Jesus standing there, but she did not realize that it was Jesus.
"Woman," he said, "why are you crying? Who is it you are looking for?"
Thinking he was the gardener, she said, "Sir, if you have carried him away, tell me where you have put him, and I will get him."

My Master!
Don't try to hold on to Me....
...for I'll return to My Father in heaven, but go and tell My disciples!
Friends, I've seen Jesus, the Lord! He's alive! He has risen! Hear what He told me!
Mary, your feelings overwhelm you!
Be sensible and reasonable. It's impossible!
Fantasies! All women's imaginations!

That same day, in the evening, two of the disciples travel from Jerusalem to Emmaus...
What a disappointment! I believed Jesus and thought He would be the Messiah the world is waiting for.
And instead He was sentenced to death and crucified like a criminal!
Yes, Cleopas, what a disappointment! I'm as confused as you are....
Shalom, friends! You seem to be sad...what are you discussing?
Try to explain; may be I can help.
Don't you know the events that shook Jerusalem these days? The things about Jesus of Nazareth?
We had hoped that He was the One who would redeem Israel..
..yes, for He was the Christ. ... But it's over. It's the...
third day since all this took place and now He's dead.
Some of our women have amazed us...
...they went to the tomb early this morning....

We're listening to you with great interest.
One hour later....

Luke 24: 13-43

Now that same day two of them were going to a village called Emmaus, about seven miles from Jerusalem. They were talking with each other about everything that had happened. As they talked and discussed these things with each other, Jesus himself came up and walked along with them; but they were kept from recognizing him.
He asked them, "What are you discussing together as you walk along?"
They stood still, their faces downcast. One of them, named Cleopas, asked him, "Are you only a visitor to Jerusalem and do not know the things that have happened there in these days?"
"What things?" he asked.
"About Jesus of Nazareth," they replied. "He was a prophet, powerful in word and deed before God and all the people. The chief priests and our rulers handed him over to be sentenced to death, and they crucified him; but we had hoped that he was the one who was going to redeem Israel. And what is more, it is the third day since all this took place. In addition, some of our women amazed us. They went to the tomb early this morning but didn't find his body. They came and told us that they had seen a vision of angels, who said he was alive. Then some of our companions went to the tomb and found it just as the women had said, but him they did not see."
He said to them, "How foolish you are, and how slow

We've arrived in Emmaus... we invite you to stay with us.

' heart to believe all that the prophets have spoken!
id not the Christ have to suffer these things and then
ıter his glory?" And beginning with Moses and all
e Prophets, he explained to them what was said in all
e Scriptures concerning himself.
s they approached the village to which they were
ıing, Jesus acted as if he were going farther. But they
ged him strongly, "Stay with us, for it is nearly
ening; the day is almost over." So he went in to stay
ıth them.
hen he was at the table with them, he took bread,
ve thanks, broke it and began to give it to them.
ıen their eyes were opened and they recognized him,
d he disappeared from their sight. They asked each
ıer, "Were not our hearts burning within us while he

talked with us on the road and opened the Scriptures to us?"
They got up and returned at once to Jerusalem. There they found the Eleven and those with them, assembled together and saying, "It is true! The Lord has risen and has appeared to Simon." Then the two told what had happened on the way, and how Jesus was recognized by them when he broke the bread.
While they were still talking about this, Jesus himself stood among them and said to them, "Peace be with you."
They were startled and frightened, thinking they saw a ghost. He said to them, "Why are you troubled, and why do doubts rise in your minds? Look at my hands and my feet. It is I myself! Touch me and see; a ghost does not have flesh and bones, as you see I have." When he had said this, he showed them his hands and feet. And while they still did not believe it because of joy and amazement, he asked them, "Do you have anything here to eat?" They gave him a piece of broiled fish, and he took it and ate it in their presence.

John 20: 19-29

On the evening of that first day of the week, when the disciples were together, with the doors locked for fear of the Jews, Jesus came and stood among them and said, "Peace be with you!" After he said this, he showed them his hands and side. The disciples were overjoyed when they saw the Lord.

Again Jesus said, "Peace be with you! As the Father has sent me, I am sending you." And with that he breathed on them and said, "Receive the Holy Spirit. If you forgive anyone his sins, they are forgiven; if you do not forgive them, they are not forgiven."

Now Thomas (called Didymus), one of the Twelve, was not with the disciples when Jesus came. So the other disciples told him, "We have seen the Lord!" But he said to them, "Unless I see the nail marks in his hands and put my finger where the nails were, and put my hand into his side, I will not believe it."

A week later his disciples were in the house again, and Thomas was with them. Though the doors were locked, Jesus came and stood among them and said, "Peace be with you!" Then he said to Thomas, "Put your finger here; see my hands. Reach out your hand and put it into my side. Stop doubting and believe."
Thomas said to him, "My Lord and my God!"
Then Jesus told him, "Because you have seen me, you have believed; blessed are those who have not seen and yet have believed."

John 21: 1-19

Afterward Jesus appeared again to his disciples, by the Sea of Tiberias. It happened this way: Simon Peter, Thomas (called Didymus), Nathanael from Cana in Galilee, the sons of Zebedee, and two other disciples were together. "I'm going out to fish," Simon Peter told them, and they said, "We'll go with you." So they went out and got into the boat, but that night they caught nothing.

Early in the morning, Jesus stood on the shore, but the

disciples did not realize that it was Jesus.
He called out to them, "Friends, haven't you any fish?"
"No," they answered.
He said, "Throw your net on the right side of the boat and you will find some." When they did, they were unable to haul the net in because of the large number of fish.
Then the disciple whom Jesus loved said to Peter, "It is the Lord!" As soon as Simon Peter heard him say, "It is the Lord," he wrapped his outer garment around him (for he had taken it off) and jumped into the water. The other disciples followed in the boat, towing the net full of fish, for they

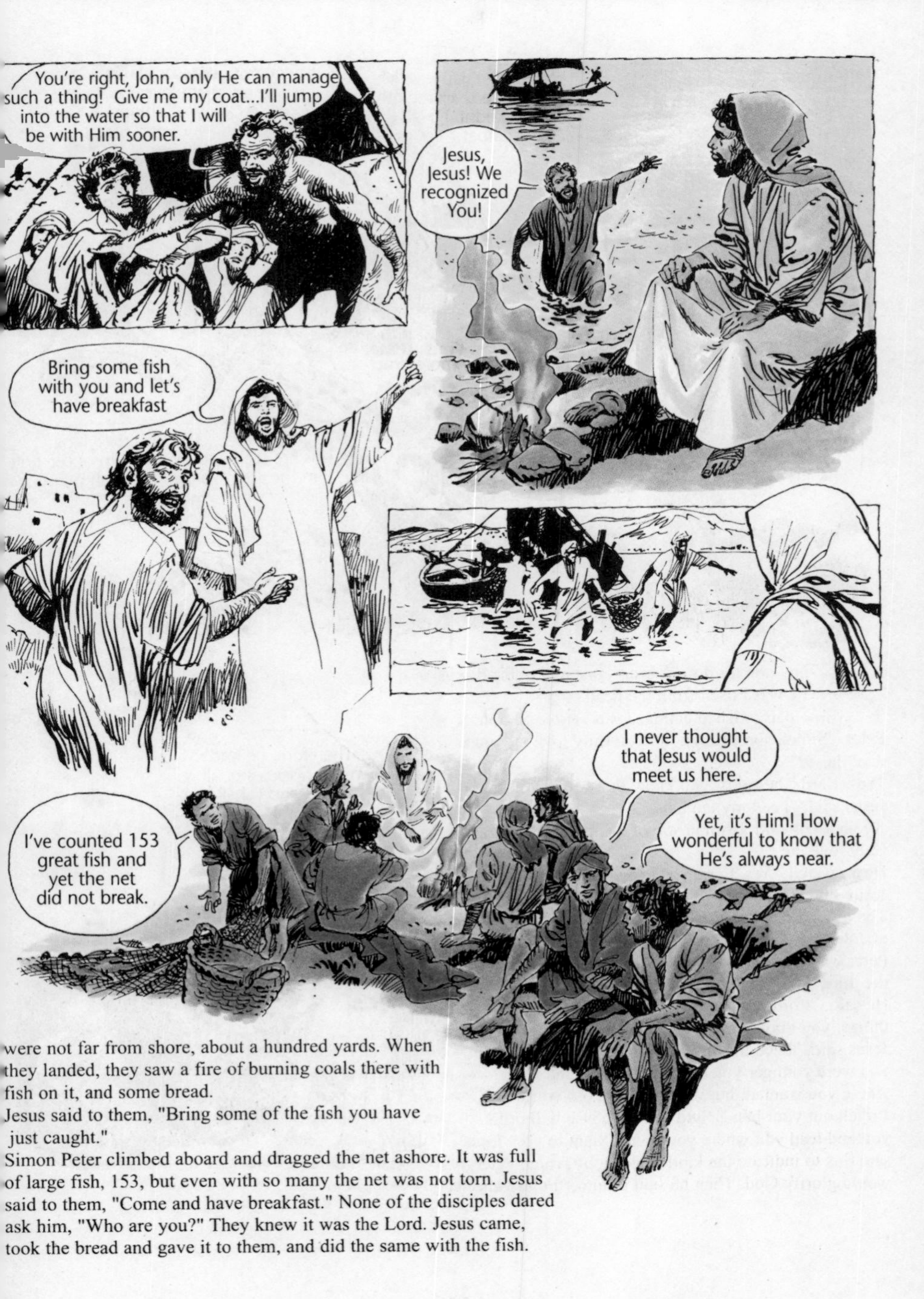

You're right, John, only He can manage such a thing! Give me my coat...I'll jump into the water so that I will be with Him sooner.
Jesus, Jesus! We recognized You!
Bring some fish with you and let's have breakfast
I've counted 153 great fish and yet the net did not break.
I never thought that Jesus would meet us here.
Yet, it's Him! How wonderful to know that He's always near.

were not far from shore, about a hundred yards. When they landed, they saw a fire of burning coals there with fish on it, and some bread.
Jesus said to them, "Bring some of the fish you have just caught."
Simon Peter climbed aboard and dragged the net ashore. It was full of large fish, 153, but even with so many the net was not torn. Jesus said to them, "Come and have breakfast." None of the disciples dared ask him, "Who are you?" They knew it was the Lord. Jesus came, took the bread and gave it to them, and did the same with the fish.

now the third time Jesus appeared to his disci-
he was raised from the dead.

had finished eating, Jesus said to Simon Peter, "Simon son of John, do you truly love me more than these?"

"Yes, Lord," he said, "you know that I love you."

Jesus said, "Feed my lambs."

Again Jesus said, "Simon son of John, do you truly love me?"

He answered, "Yes, Lord, you know that I love you."

Jesus said, "Take care of my sheep."

The third time he said to him, "Simon son of John, do you love me?"

Peter was hurt because Jesus asked him the third time, "Do you love me?"

He said, "Lord, you know all things; you know that I love you."

Jesus said, "Feed my sheep. I tell you the truth, when you were younger you dressed yourself and went where you wanted; but when you are old you will stretch out your hands, and someone else will dress you and lead you where you do not want to go." Jesus said this to indicate the kind of death by which Peter would glorify God. Then he said to him, "Follow me!"

God's love for you

For God so loved the world, that he gave his one and only Son, that whoever believes in Him, shall not perish, but have eternal life. (John 3:16)

But God demonstrates his own love for us in this: While we were still sinners, Christ died for us. (Romans 5:8)

Jesus answered: I am the way and the truth and the life. No one comes to the Father except through me. (John 14:6)

And the blood of Jesus, his Son, purifies us from all sin. If we claim to be without sin, we deceive ourselves and the truth is not in us. If we confess our sins, he is faithful and just and will forgive us our sins and purify us from all unrighteousness. (1 John 1:7-9)

God, have mercy on me, a sinner. (Luke 18:13)

Believe in the Lord Jesus, and you will be saved. (Acts 16:31)

the Good News is:

Jesus has risen from the dead

He Lives!

Prayer: Jesus, I believe with all my heart,
that you also died for my sins.
I confess all my sins and ask for your forgiveness.
Come and live in my heart,
from now on in my life it shall be:
Not my will, but your will shall be done.
I thank you that you want to be my Saviour.

Amen!

Matthew

The Beatitudes

5 Now when he saw the crowds, he went up on a mountainside and sat down. His disciples came to him, [2]and he began to teach them, saying:

[3]"Blessed are the poor in spirit,
for theirs is the kingdom of heaven.
[4]Blessed are those who mourn,
for they will be comforted.
[5]Blessed are the meek,
for they will inherit the earth.
[6]Blessed are those who hunger and thirst for righteousness,
for they will be filled.
[7]Blessed are the merciful,
for they will be shown mercy.
[8]Blessed are the pure in heart,
for they will see God.
[9]Blessed are the peacemakers,
for they will be called sons of God.
[10]Blessed are those who are persecuted because of righteousness,
for theirs is the kingdom of heaven.

[11]"Blessed are you when people insult you, persecute you and falsely say all kinds of evil against you because of me. [12]Rejoice and be glad, because great is your reward in heaven, for in the same way they persecuted the prophets who were before you.

Salt and Light

[13]"You are the salt of the earth. But if the salt loses its saltiness, how can it be made salty again? It is no longer good for anything, except to be thrown out and trampled by men.

[14]"You are the light of the world. A city on a hill cannot be hidden. [15]Neither do people light a lamp and put it under a bowl. Instead they put it on its stand, and it gives light to everyone in the house. [16]In the same way, let your light shine before men, that they may see your good deeds and praise your Father in heaven.

The Fulfillment of the Law

[17]"Do not think that I have come to abolish the Law or the Prophets; I have not come to abolish them but to fulfill them. [18]I tell you the truth, until heaven and earth disappear, not the smallest letter, not the least stroke of a pen, will by any means disappear from the Law until everything is accomplished. [19]Anyone who breaks one of the least of these commandments and teaches others to do the same will be called least in the kingdom of heaven, but whoever practices and teaches these commands will be called great in the kingdom of heaven. [20]For I tell you that unless your righteousness surpasses that

of the Pharisees and the teachers of he law, you will certainly not enter he kingdom of heaven.

Murder

[21]"You have heard that it was said o the people long ago, 'Do not nurder,[a] and anyone who murders vill be subject to judgment.' [22]But I ell you that anyone who is angry vith his brother[b] will be subject to udgment. Again, anyone who says o his brother, 'Raca,[c]' is answerable o the Sanhedrin. But anyone who ays, 'You fool!' will be in danger of he fire of hell.

[23]"Therefore, if you are offering our gift at the altar and there emember that your brother has omething against you, [24]leave your gift there in front of the altar. First go and be reconciled to your rother; then come and offer your gift.

[25]"Settle matters quickly with your dversary who is taking you to ourt. Do it while you are still with im on the way, or he may hand you ver to the judge, and the judge may and you over to the officer, and you nay be thrown into prison. [26]I tell ou the truth, you will not get out ntil you have paid the last penny,[d]

dultery

[27]"You have heard that it was said, Do not commit adultery.'[e] [28]But I tell ou that anyone who looks at a voman lustfully has already committed adultery with her in his eart, [29]If your right eye causes you o sin, gouge it out and throw it way. It is better for you to lose one part of your body than for your whole body to be thrown into hell. [30]And if your right hand causes you to sin, cut it off and throw it away. It is better for you to lose one part of your body than for your whole body to go into hell.

Divorce

[31]"If has been said, 'Anyone who divorces his wife must give her a certificate of divorce.'[a] [32]But I tell you that anyone who divorces his wife, except for marital unfaithfulness, causes her to become an adulteress, and anyone who marries the divorced woman commits adultery.

Oaths

[33]"Again, you have heard that it was said to the people long ago, 'Do not break your oath, but keep the oaths you have made to the Lord.' [34]But I tell you. Do not swear at all: either by heaven, for it is God's throne; [35]or by the earth, for it is his footstool; or by Jerusalem, for it is the city of the Great King. [36]And do not swear by your head, for you cannot make even one hair white or black. [37]Simply let your 'Yes' be 'Yes,' and your 'No,' 'No'; anything beyond this comes from the evil one.

An Eye for an Eye

[38] You have heard that it was said, 'Eye for eye, and tooth for tooth.'[b] [39]But I tell you. Do not resist an evil person. If someone strikes you on the right cheek, turn to him the other also. [40]And if someone wants to sue you and take your tunic, let him

have your cloak as well. [41]If someone forces you to go one mile, go with him two miles. [42]Give to the one who asks you, and do not turn away from the one who wants to borrow from you.

Love for Enemies

[43]"You have heard that it was said, 'Love your neighbor[c] and hate your enemy.' [44]But I tell you: Love your enemies[d] and pray for those who persecute you, [45]that you may be sons of your Father in heaven. He causes his sun to rise on the evil and the good, and sends rain on the righteous and the unrighteous. [46]If you love those who love you, what reward will you get? Are not even the tax collectors doing that? [47]And if you greet only your brothers, what are you doing more than others? Do not even pagans do that? [48]Be perfect, therefore, as your heavenly Father is perfect.

Giving to the Needy

6 "Be careful not to do your 'acts of righteousness' before men, to be seen by them. If you do, you will have no reward from your Father in heaven.

[2]"So when you give to the needy, do not announce it with trumpets, as the hypocrites do in the synagogues and on the streets, to be honored by men. I tell you the truth, they have received their reward in full. [3]But when you give to the needy, do not let your left hand know what your right hand is doing, [4]so that your giving may be in secret. Then your Father, who sees what is done in secret, will reward you.

Prayer

[5]"And when you pray, do not be like the hypocrites, for they love to pray standing in the synagogues and on the street corners to be seen by men. I tell you the truth, they have received their reward in full. [6]But when you pray, go into your room, close the door and pray to your Father, who is unseen. Then your Father, who sees what is done in secret, will reward you. [7]And when you pray, do not keep on babbling like pagans, for they think they will be heard because of their many words. [8]Do not be like them, for your Father knows what you need before you ask him.

[9]"This, then, is how you should pray:

" "Our Father in heaven, hallowed be your name,
[10]your kingdom come,
your will be done
on earth as it is in heaven.
[11]Give us today our daily bread.
[12]Forgive us our debts,
as we also have forgiven
our debtors.
[13]And lead us not into temptation,
but deliver us from the evil one.[a]"

[14]For if you forgive men when they sin against you, your heavenly Father will also forgive you. [15]But if you do not forgive men their sins, your Father will not forgive your sins.

Fasting

[16]"When you fast, do not look somber as the hypocrites do, for

ıey disfigure their faces to show ıen they are fasting. I tell you the ·uth, they have received their eward in full. [17]But when you fast, ut oil on your head and wash your ıce, [18]so that it will not be obvious) men that you are fasting, but only) your Father, who is unseen; and our Father, who sees what is done ı secret, will reward you.

reasures in Heaven

[19]"Do not store up for yourselves easures on earth, where moth and ıst destroy, and where thieves reak in and steal. [20]But store up ror ourselves treasures in heaven here moth and rust do not destroy, ıd where thieves do not break in ıd steal. [21]For where your treasure , there your heart will be also. [22]"The eye is the lamp of the body. your eyes are good, your whole ody will be full of light. [23]But if our eyes are bad, your whole body ill be full of darkness. If then the ght within you is darkness, how eat is that darkness!

[24]"No one can serve two masters. ither he will hate the one and love e other, or he will be devoted to e one and despise the other. You ınnot serve both God and Money.

o Not Worry

[25]"Therefore I tell you, do not orry about your life, what you will t or drink; or about your body, hat you will wear. Is not life more ıportant than food, and the body ore important than clothes? ook at the birds of the air; they , not sow or reap or store away in barns, and yet your heavenly Father feeds them. Are you not much more valuable than they? [27]Who of you by worrying can add a single hour to his life [a]?

[28]"And why do you worry about clothes? See how the lilies of the field grow. They do not labor or spin. [29]Yet I tell you that not even Solomon in all his splendor was dressed like one of these, [30]If that is how God clothes the grass of the field,which is here today and tomorrow is thrown into the fire, will he not much more clothe you, O you of little faith? [31]So do not worry, saying, 'What shall we eat?' or 'What shall we drink?' or 'What shall we wear?' [32]For the pagans run after all these things, and your heavenly Father knows that you need them. [33]But seek first his kingdom and his righteousness, and all these things will be given to you as well. [34]Therefore do not worry about tomorrow, for tomorrow will worry about itself. Each day has enough trouble of its own.

Judging Others

7 "Do not judge, or you too will be judged. [2]For in the same way you judge others, you will be judged, and with the measure you use, it will be measured to you. [3]"Why do you look at the speck of sawdust in your brother's eye and pay no attention to the plank in your own eye? [4]How can you say to your brother, 'Let me take the speck out of your eye,' when all the time there is a plank in your own eye? [5]You hypocrite, first take the plank out of

your own eye, and then you will see clearly to remove the speck from your brother's eye.

[6]"Do not give dogs what is sacred; do not throw your pearls to pigs. If you do, they may trample them under their feet, and then turn and tear you to pieces.

Ask, Seek, Knock

[7]"Ask and it will be given to you; seek and you will find; knock and the door will be opened to you. [8]For everyone who asks receives; he who seeks finds; and to him who knocks, the door will be opened.

[9]"Which of you, if his son asks for bread, will give him a stone? [10]Or if he asks for a fish, will give him a snake? [11]If you, then, though you are evil, know how to give good gifts to your children, how much more will your Father in heaven give good gifts to those who ask him! [12]So in everything, do to others what you would have them do to you, for this sums up the Law and the Prophets.

The Narrow and Wide Gates

[13]"Enter through the narrow gate. For wide is the gate and broad is the road that leads to destruction, and many enter through it. [14]But small is the gate and narrow the road that leads to life, and only a few find it.

A Tree and Its Fruit

[15]"Which out for false prophets. They come to you in sheep's clothing, but inwardly they are ferocious wolves. [16]By their fruit you will recognize them. Do people pick grapes from thornbushes, or figs from thistles? [17]Likewise every good tree bears good fruit, but a bad tree bears bad fruit. [18]A good tre cannot bear bad fruit, and a bad tre cannot bear good fruit. [19]Every tre that does not bear good fruit is cu down and thrown into the fire [20]Thus, by their fruit you wil recognize them.

[21]"Not everyone who says to me 'Lord, Lord,' will enter the kingdon of heaven, but only he who does th will of my Father who is in heaven [22]Many will say to me on that day 'Lord, Lord, did we not prophesy i your name, and in your name driv out demons and perform man miracles?' [23]Then I will tell then plainly, 1 never knew you. Awa from me, you evildoers!'

The Wise and Foolish Builders

[24]"Therefore everyone who hear these words of mine and puts ther into practice is like a wise man wh built his house on the rock. [25]Th rain came down, the streams rose and the winds blew and beat agains that house; yet it did not fal because it had its foundation on th rock. [26]But everyone who hear these words of mine and does nc put them into practice is like foolish man who built his house o sand. [27]The rain came down, th streams rose, and the winds ble and beat against that house, and fell with a great crash."

[28]When Jesus had finished sayin these things, the crowds wer amazed at his teaching, [29]because h taught as one who had authorit and not as their teachers of the law.

James

1 James, a servant of God and of the Lord Jesus Christ,

To the twelve tribes scattered among the nations:

Greetings.

Trials and Temptations

[2]Consider it pure joy, my brothers, whenever you face trials of many kinds, [3]because you know that the testing of your faith develops perseverance. [4]Perseverance must finish its work so that you may be mature and complete, not lacking anything. [5]If any of you lacks wisdom, he should ask God, who gives generously to all without finding fault, and it will be given to him. [6]But when he asks, he must believe and not doubt, because he who doubts is like a wave of the sea, blown and tossed by the wind. [7]That man should not think he will receive anything from the Lord; [8]he is a double-minded man, unstable in all he does.

[9]The brother in humble circumstances ought to take pride in his high position. [10]But the' one who is rich should take pride in his low position, because he will pass away like a wild flower. [11]For the sun rises with scorching heat and withers the plant; its blossom falls and its beauty is destroyed. In the same way, the rich man will fade away even while he goes about his business.

[12]Blessed is the man who perseveres under trial, because when he has stood the test, he will receive the crown of life that God has promised to those who love him.

[13]When tempted, no one should say, "God is tempting me." For God cannot be tempted by evil, nor does he tempt anyone; [14]but each one is tempted when, by his own evil desire, he is dragged away and enticed. [15]Then, after desire has conceived, it gives birth to sin; and sin, when it is full-grown, gives birth to death.

[16]Don't be deceived, my dear brothers, [17]Every good and perfect gift is from above, coming down from the Father of the heavenly lights, who does not change like shifting shadows. [18]He chose to give us birth through the word of truth, that we might be a kind of first fruits of all he created.

Listening and Doing

[19]My dear brothers, take note of this: Everyone should be quick to listen, slow to speak and slow to become angry, [20]for man's anger does not bring about the righteous life that God desires. [21]Therefore, get rid of all moral filth and the evil that is so prevalent and humbly accept the word planted in you, which can save you.

[22]Do not merely listen to the word, and so deceive your- selves. Do what it says. [23]Anyone who listens

to the word but does not do what it says is like a man who looks at his face in a mirror [24]and, after looking at himself, goes away and immediately forgets what he looks like. [25]But the man who looks intently into the perfect law that gives freedom, and continues to do this, not forgetting what he has heard, but doing it----he will be blessed in what he does. [26]If anyone considers himself religious and yet does not keep a tight rein on his tongue, he deceives himself and his religion is worthless. [27]Religion that God our Father accepts as pure and faultless is this: to look after orphans and widows in their distress and to keep oneself from being polluted by the world.

Favoritism Forbidden

2 My brothers, as believers in our glorious Lord Jesus Christ, don't show favoritism. [2]Suppose a man comes into your meeting wearing a gold ring and the clothes, and a poor man in shabby clothes also comes in. [3]If you show special attention to the man wearing fine clothes and say, "Here's a good seat for you," but say to the poor man, "You stand there" or "Sit on the floor by my feet," [4]have you not discriminated among yourselves and become judges with evil thoughts?

[5]Listen, my dear brothers: Has not God chosen those who are poor in the eyes of the world to be rich in faith and to inherit the kingdom he promised those who love him? [6]But you have insulted the poor. Is it no the rich who are exploiting you Are they not the ones who ar dragging you into court? [7]Are the not the ones who are slandering th noble name of him to whom yo belong?

[8]If you really keep the royal lav found in Scripture, "Love you neighbor as yourself,"[a] you ar doing right. [9]But if you shov favoritism, you sin and are con noted by the law as law- breakers [10]For whoever keeps the whole lav and yet stumbles at just one point i guilty of breaking all of it. [11]For h who said, "Do not commi adultery,"[b] also said, "Do no murder."[c] If you do not commi adultery but do commit murder, yo have become a law-breaker.

[12]Speak and act as those who ar going to be judged by the law tha gives freedom, [13]because judgmen without mercy will be shown t anyone who has not been merciful Mercy triumphs over judgment!

Faith and Deeds

[14]What good is it, my brothers, if a man claims to have faith but has n deeds? Can such faith save him [15]Suppose a brother or sister i without clothes and daily food. [16]I one of you says to him, "Go, I wisl you well; keep warm and well fed," but does nothing about his physica needs, what good is it? [17]In the sam way, faith by itself, if it is no accompanied by action, is dead.

[18]But someone will say, "You hav faith; I have deeds."

Show me your faith withou

deeds, and I will show you my faith by what I do. [19]You believe that there is one God. Good! Even the demons believe that---and shudder.

[20]You foolish man, do you want evidence that faith with-out deeds is useless[d] ? [21]Was not our ancestor Abraham considered righteous for what he did when he offered his son Isaac on the altar? [22]You see that his faith and his actions were working together, and his faith was made complete by what he did. [23]And the scripture was ful-filled that says, 'Abraham believed God, and it was credited to him as righteousness,"[e] and he was called God's friend. [24]You see that a person is justified by what he does and not by faith alone.

[25]In the same way, was not even Rahab the prostitute considered righteous for what she did when she gave lodging to the spies and sent them off in a different direction? [26]As the body without the spirit is dead, so faith without deeds is dead.

Taming the Tongue

3 Not many of you should presume to be teachers, my brothers, because you know that we who teach will be judged more strictly. [2]We all stumble in many ways. If any-one is never at fault in what he says, he is a perfect man, able to keep his whole body in check.

[3]When we put bits into the mouths of horses to make them obey us, we can turn the whole animal. [4]Or take ships as an example. Although they are so large and are driven by strong winds, they are steered by a very small rudder wherever the pilot wants to go. [5]Likewise the tongue is a small part of the body, but it makes great boasts. Consider what a great forest is set on fire by a small spark. [6]The tongue also is a fire, a world of evil among the parts of the body. It corrupts the whole person, sets the whole course of his life on fire, and is itself set on fire by hell.

[7]All kinds of animals, birds, reptiles and creatures of the sea are being tamed and have been tamed by man, [8]but no man can tame the tongue. It is a restless evil, full of deadly poison.

[9]With the tongue we praise our Lord and Father, and with it we curse men, who have been made in God's likeness. [10]Out of the same mouth come praise and cursing. My brothers, this should not be. [11]Can both fresh water and salt[a] water flow from the same spring? [12]My brothers, can a fig tree bear olives, or a grapevine bear figs? Neither can a salt spring produce fresh water.

Two Kinds of Wisdom

[13]Who is wise and understanding among you? Let him show it by his good life, by deeds done in the humility that comes from wisdom. [14]But if you harbor bitter envy and selfish ambition in your hearts, do not boast about it or deny the truth. [15]Such "wisdom" does not come down from heaven but is earthly, unspiritual, of the devil. [16]For where you have envy and selfish ambition, there you find disorder and every evil practice.

[17]But the wisdom that comes from heaven is first of all pure; then peace-loving, considerate, submissive, full of mercy' and good fruit, impartial and sincere. [18]Peacemakers who sow in peace raise a harvest of righteousness.

Submit Yourselves to God

4 What causes fights and quarrels among you? Don't they come from your desires that battle within you? [2]You want something but don't get it. You kill and covet, but you cannot have what you want. You quarrel and fight. You do not have, because you do not ask God. [3]When you ask, you do not receive, because you ask with wrong motives, that you may spend what you get on your pleasures.

[4]You adulterous people, don't you know that friendship with the world is hatred toward God? Anyone who chooses to be a friend of the world becomes an enemy of God. [5]Or do you think Scripture says without reason that the spirit he caused to live in us envies intensely? [6]But he gives us more grace. That is why Scripture says:

"God opposes the proud but gives grace to the humble."[b]

[7]Submit yourselves, then, to God. Resist the devil, and he will flee from you. [8]Come near to God and he will come near to you. Wash you hands, you sinners, and purify you hearts, you double-minded [9]Grieve, mourn and wail. Change your laughter to mourning and you joy to gloom. [10]Humble your selves before the Lord, and he will lift you up.

[11]Brothers, do not slander one another. Anyone who speaks against his brother or judges him speaks against the law and judges it When you judge the law, you are no keeping it, but sitting in judgmen on it. [12]There is only one Law-give and Judge, the one who is able to save and destroy. But you who are you to judge your neighbor?

Boasting About Tomorrow

[13]Now listen, you who say, 'Today or tomorrow we will go to this o that city, spend a year there, carry on business and make money." [14]Why you do not even know what wil happen tomorrow. What is you life? You are a mist that appears fo a little while and hen vanishes [15]Instead, you ought to say, "If it i the Lord's will we will live and do this or that. [16]As it is, you boast and brag. All such boasting is evil [17]Anyone, then, who knows the good he ought to do and doesn't do it, sins.

I Peter

1 Peter, an apostle of Jesus Christ,

To God's elect, strangers. the world, scattered throughout Pontus

Galatia, Cappadoci Asia and Bithynia, [2]Who have been chosen according to the foreknowledge of God the Father, through the sanctifying work of the Spirit, for obedience to Jesus Christ and sprinkling by his blood:

Grace and peace be yours in abundance.

Praise to God for a Living Hope

[3]Praise be to the God and Father of our Lord Jesus Christ! In his great mercy he has given us new birth into a living hope through the resurrection of Jesus Christ from the dead, [4]and into an inheritance that can never perish, spoil or fade---- kept in heaven for you, [5]who through faith are shielded by God's power until the coming of the salvation that is ready to be revealed in the last time. [6]In this you greatly rejoice, though now for a little while you may have had to suffer grief in all kinds of trials. [7]These have come so that your faith of greater worth than gold, which perishes even though refined by fire---may be proved genuine and may result in praise, glory and honor when Jesus Christ is revealed. [8]Though you have not seen him, you love him; and even though you do not see him now, you believe in him and are filled with an inexpressible and glorious joy, [9]for you are receiving the goal of your faith, the salvation of your souls.

[10]Concerning this salvation, the prophets, who spoke of the grace that was to come to you, searched intently and with the greatest care, [11]trying to find out the time and circumstances to which the Spirit of Christ in them was pointing when he predicted the sufferings of Christ and the glories that would follow, [12]It was revealed to them that they were not serving themselves but you, when they spoke of the things that have now been told you by those who have preached the gospel to you by the Holy Spirit sent from heaven. Even angels long to look into these things.

Be Holy

[13]Therefore, prepare your minds for action; be self-controlled; set your hope fully on the grace to be given you when Jesus Christ is revealed. [14]As obedient children, do not conform to the evil desires you had when you lived in ignorance. [15]But just as he who called you is holy, so be holy in all you do; [16]for it is written: "Be holy, because I am holy."[a]

[17]Since you call on a Father who judges each man's work impartially, live your lives as strangers here in reverent fear. [18]For you know that it was not with perishable things such as silver or gold that you were redeemed from the empty way of life handed down to you from your forefathers, [19]but with the precious blood of Christ, a lamb without blemish or defect. [20]He was chosen before the creation of the world, but was revealed in these last times for

your sake. [21]Through him you believe in God, who raised him from the dead and glorified him, and so your faith and hope are in God.

[22]Now that you have purified your selves by obeying the truth so that you have sincere love for your brothers, love one another deeply, from the heart,[b] [23]For you have been born again, not of perishable seed, but of imperishable, through the living and enduring word of God. [24]For,

"All men are like grass, and all
their glory is like the flowers of
the field;
the grass withers and the
flowers fall,
[25]but the word of the Lord stands
forever."[a]

And this is the word that was preached to you.

2 Therefore, rid yourselves of all malice and all deceit, hypocrisy, envy, and slander of every kind. [2]Like newborn babies, crave pure spiritual milk, so that by it you may grow up in your salvation, [3]now that you have tasted that the Lord is good.

The Living Stone and a Chosen People

[4]As you come to him, the living Stone---rejected by men but chosen by God and precious to him [5]you also, like living stones, are being built into a spiritual house to be a holy priesthood, offering spiritual sacrifices acceptable to God through Jesus Christ. [6]For in Scripture it says:

"See, I lay a stone in Zion,
a chosen and precious
cornerstone,
and the one who trusts in
him
will never be put to shame."[b]

[7]Now to you who believe, this stone is precious. But to those who do not believe,

"The stone the builders rejected
has become the capstone,"[c,d]
[8]and,
"A stone that causes men to
stumble
and a rock that makes them
fall."[c]

They stumble because they disobey the message---which is also what they were destined for.

[9]But you are a chosen people, a royal priesthood, a holy nation, a people belonging to God, that you may declare the praises of him who called you out of darkness into his wonderful light. [10]Once you were not a people, but now you are the people of God; once you had not received mercy, but now you have received mercy.

[11]Dear friends, I urge you, as aliens and strangers in the world, to abstain from sinful desires, which war against your soul. [12]Live such good lives among the pagans that, though they accuse you of doing wrong, they may see your good deeds and glorify God on the day he visits us.

Submission to Rulers and Masters

[13]Submit yourselves for the Lord's sake to every authority instituted among men: whether to the king, as the supreme authority, [14]Or to governors, who are sent by him to punish those who do wrong and to commend those who do right. [15]For it is God's will that by doing good you should silence the ignorant talk of foolish men. [16]Live as free men, but do not use your freedom as a cover-up for evil; live as servants of God. [17]Show proper respect to everyone: Love the brotherhood of believers, fear God, honor the king.

[18]Slaves, submit yourselves to your masters with all respect, not only to those who are good and considerate, but also to those who are harsh. [19]For it is commendable if a man bears up under the pain of unjust suffering because he is conscious of God. [20]But how is it to your credit if you receive a beating for doing wrong and endure it? But if you suffer for doing good and you endure it, this is commendable before God. [21]To this you were called, because Christ suffered for you, leaving you an example, that you should follow in his steps.

[22]"He committed no sin,
and no deceit was found in
his mouth,"[a]

[23]When they hurled their insults at him, he did not retaliate; when he suffered, he made no threats. Instead, he entrusted himself to him who judges justly. [24]He himself bore our sins in his body on the tree, so that we might die to sins and live for righteousness; by his wounds you have been healed. [25]For you were like sheep going astray, but now you have returned to the Shepherd and Overseer of your souls.

Wives and Husbands

3 Wives, in the same way be submissive to your husbands so that, if any of them do not believe the word, they may be won over without words by the behavior of their wives, [2]when they see the purity and reverence of your lives. [3]Your beauty should not come from outward adornment, such as braided hair and the wearing of gold jewelry and fine clothes. [4]Instead, it should be that of your inner self, the unfading beauty of a gentle and quiet spirit, which is of great worth in God's sight. [5]For this is the way the holy women of the past who put their hope in God used to make themselves beautiful. They were submissive to their own husbands, [6]like Sarah, who obeyed Abraham and called him her master. You are her daughters if you do what is right and do not give way to fear.

[7]Husbands, in the same way be considerate as you live with your wives, and treat them with respect as the weaker partner and as heirs with you of the gracious gift of life, so that nothing will hinder your prayers.

Suffering for Doing Good

[8]Finally, all of you, live in harmony

with one another; be sympathetic, love as brothers, be compassionate and humble. [9]Do not repay evil with evil or insult with insult, but with blessing, because to this you were called so that you may inherit a blessing. [10]For,

"Whoever would love life and see good days
must keep his tongue from evil
and his lips from deceitful speech.
[11]He must turn from evil and do good; he must seek peace and pursue it.
[12]For the eyes of the Lord are on the righteous and his ears are attentive to their prayer, but the face of the Lord is against those who do evil."[a]

[13]Who is going to harm you if you are eager to do good? [14]But even if you should suffer for what is right, you are blessed. "Do not fear what they fear , do not be frightened."[c] [15]But in your hearts set apart Christ as Lord. Always be prepared to give an answer to everyone who asks you to- give the reason for the hope that you have. But do this with gentleness and respect, [16]keeping a clear conscience, so that those who speak maliciously against your good behavior in Christ may be ashamed of their slander, [17]It is better, if it is God's will, to suffer for doing good than for doing evil. [18]For Christ died for sins once for all, the righteous for the unrighteous, to bring you to God. He was put to death in the body but made alive by the Spirit, [19]through whom[d] also he went and preached to the. spirits in prison [20]Who disobeyed long ago when God waited patiently in the days of Noah while the ark was being built. In it only a few people, eight in all, were saved through water, [21]and this water symbolizes baptism that now saves you also---not the removal of dirt from the body but the pledge[e] of a good conscience toward God. It saves you by the resurrection of Jesus Christ, [22]Who has gone into heaven and is at God's right hand---with angels, authorities and powers in submission to him.

Living for God

4 Therefore, since Christ suffered in his body, arm yourselves also with the same attitude, because he who has suffered in his body is done with sin. [2]As a result, he does not live the rest of his earthly life for evil human desires, but rather for the will of God. [3]For you have spent enough time in the past doing what pagans choose to do---living in debauchery, lust, drunkenness, orgies, carousing and detestable idolatry. [4]They think it strange that you do not plunge with them into the same flood of dissipation, and they heap abuse on you. [5]But they will have to give account to him who is ready to judge the living and the dead. [6]For this is the reason the gospel was preached even to those who are now dead, so that they might be judged according to men in regard to the body, but live according to God in regard to the spirit.

[7]The end of all things is near. Therefore be clear minded and self-controlled so that you can pray. [8]Above all, love each other deeply, because love covers over a multitude of sins. [9]Offer hospitality to one another without grumbling. [10]Each one should use whatever gift he has received to serve others, faithfully administering God's grace in its various forms. [11]If anyone speaks, he should do it as one speaking the very words of God. If anyone serves, he should do it with the strength God provides, so that in all things God may be praised through Jesus Christ. To him be the glory and the power tor ever and ever. Amen.

Suffering for Being a Christian

[12]Dear friends, do not be surprised at the painful trial you are suffering, as though something strange were happening to you. [13]But rejoice that you participate in the sufferings of Christ, so that you may be overjoyed when his glory is revealed. [14]If you are insulted because of the name of Christ, you are blessed, for the Spirit of glory and of God rests on you. [15]If you suffer, it should not be as a murderer or thief or any other kind of criminal, or even as a meddler. [16]However, if you suffer as a Christian, do not be ashamed, but praise God that you bear that name. [17]For it is time for judgment to begin with the family of God; and if it begins with us, what will the outcome be for those who do not obey the gospel of God? [18]And,

"If it is hard for the righteous
to be saved,
what will become of the
ungodly and the sinner?"[a]

[19]So then, those who suffer according to God's will should commit themselves to their faithful Creator and continue to do good.

I Corinthians 15

The Resurrection of Christ

15 Now, brothers, I want to I remind you of the gospel I preached to you, which you received and on which you have taken your stand. [2]By this gospel you are saved, if you hold firmly to the word I preached to you. Other wise, you have believed in vain.

[3]For what I received I passed on to you as of first importance[b]: that Christ died for our sins according to the Scriptures, [4]that he was buried, that he was raised on the third day according to the Scriptures, sand that he appeared to Peter,[c] and then to the Twelve. [5]After that, he appeared to more than five hundred of the brothers at the same time, most of whom are still living, though some have fallen asleep. [7]Then he appeared to James, then to all the apostles, [8]and last of all he appeared to me also, as to one ab-

normally born.

[9]For I am the least of the apostles and do not even deserve to be called an apostle, because I persecuted the church of God. [10]But by the grace of God I am what I am, and his grace to me was not without effect. No, I worked harder than all of them---yet not I, but the grace of God that was with me. [11]Whether, then, it was I or they, this is what we preach, and this is what you believed.

The Resurrection of the Dead

[12]But if it is preached that Christ has been raised from the dead, how can some of you say that there is no resurrection of the dead? [13]If there is no resurrection of the dead, then not even Christ has been raised. [14]And if Christ has not been raised, our preaching is useless and so is your faith. [15]More than that, we are then found to be false witnesses about God, for we have testified about God that he raised Christ from the dead. But he did not raise him if in fact the dead are not raised. [16]For if the dead are not raised, then Christ has not been raised either. [17]And if Christ has not been raised, your faith is futile; you are still in your sins. [18]Then those also who have fallen asleep in Christ are lost. [19]If only for this life we have hope in Christ, we are to be pitied more than all men.

[20]But Christ has indeed been raised from the dead, the first-fruits of those who have fallen asleep. [21]For since death came through a man, the resurrection of the dead comes also through a man. [22]For as in Adam all die, so in Christ all will be made alive. [23]But each in his own turn: Christ, the firstfruits; then, when he comes, those who belong to him. [24]Then the end will come, when he hands over the kingdom to God the Father after he has destroyed all dominion, authority and power. [25]For he must reign until he has put all his enemies under his feet. [26]The last enemy to be destroyed is death. [27]For he "has put everything under his feet."[a] Now when it says that "everything" has been put under him, it is clear that this does not include God himself, who put everything under Christ. [28]When he has done this, then the Son himself will be made subject to him who put everything under him, so that God may be all in all.

[29]Now if there is no resurrection, what will those do who are baptized for the dead? If the dead are not raised at all, why are people baptized for them? [30]And as for us, why do we en- danger ourselves every hour? [31]I die every day---1 mean that, brothers---just as surely as I glory over you in Christ Jesus our Lord. [32]If I fought wild beasts in Ephesus for merely human reasons, what have I gained? If the dead are not raised,

"Let us eat and drink,
for tomorrow we die."[b]

[33]Do not be misled: "Bad company corrupts good character." [34]Come back to your senses as you ought, and stop sinning; for there are some

who are ignorant of God I say this to your shame.

The Resurrection Body

[35]But someone may ask, "How are the dead raised? With what kind of body will they come?" [36]How foolish! What you sow does not come to life unless it dies. [37]When you sow, you do not plant the body that will be, but just a seed, perhaps of wheat or of something else. [38]But God gives it a body as he has determined, and to each kind of seed he gives its own body. [39]All flesh is not the same: Men have one kind of flesh, animals have another, birds another and fish another. [40]There are also heavenly bodies and there are earthly bodies; but the splendor of the heavenly bodies is one kind, and the splendor of the earthly bodies is another. [41]The sun has one kind of splendor, the moon another and the stars another; and star differs from star in splendor.

[42]So will it be with the resurrection of the dead. The body that is sown is perishable, it is raised imperishable; [43]it is sown in dishonor, it is raised in glory; it is sown in weakness, it is raised in power; [44]if is sown a natural body, it is raised a spiritual body.

If there is a natural body, there is also a spiritual body. [45]So it is written: "The first man Adam became a living being"[a]; the last Adam, a life-giving spirit. [46]The spiritual did not come first, but the natural, and after that the spiritual. [47]The first man was of the dust of the earth, the second man from heaven. [48]As was the earthly man, so are those who are of the earth; and as is the man from heaven, so also are those who are of heaven. [49]And just as we have borne the likeness of the earthly man, so shall We[b] bear the likeness of the man from heaven.

[50]I declare to you, brothers, that flesh and blood cannot inherit the kingdom of God, nor does the perishable inherit the imperishable. [51]Listen, I tell you a mystery: We will not all sleep, but we will all be changed [52]in a flash, in the twinkling of an eye, at the last trumpet. For the trumpet will sound, the dead will be raised imperishable, and we will be changed.

[53]For the perishable must clothe itself with the imperishable, and, the mortal with immortality. [54]When the perishable has been clothed with the imperishable, and the mortal with immortality, then the saying that is written will come true: "Death has been swallowed up in victory."[c]

[55]"Where, O death, is your victory?
Where, O death, is your sting?"[d]

[56]The sting of death is sin, and the power of sin is the law. [57]But thanks be to God! He gives us the victory through our Lord Jesus Christ.

[55]Therefore, my dear brothers, stand firm. Let nothing move you. Always give yourselves fully to the work of the Lord, because you know that your labor in the Lord is not in vain.

The Lost Son

[11]Jesus continued: "There was a man who had two sons. [12]The younger one said to his father, 'Father, give me my share of the estate.' So he divided his property between them.

[13]"Not long after that, the younger son got together all he had, set off for a distant country and there squandered his wealth in wild living. [14]After he had spent everything, then was a severe famine in that whole country, and he began to be in need. [15]So he went and hired himself out to a citizen of that country, who sent him to his fields to feed pigs. [16]He longed to fill his stomach with the pods that the pigs were eating, but no one gave him anything.

[17]"When he came to his senses, he said, 'How many of my father's hired men have food to spare, and here I am starving to death! [18]I will set out and go back to my father and say to him: Father, I have sinned against heaven and against you. [19] I am no longer worthy to be called your son; make me like one of your hired men,' [20]So he got up and went to his father.

"But while he was still a long way off, his father saw him and was filled with compassion for him; he ran to his son, threw his arms around him and kissed him.

[21]"The son said to him, 'Father, I have sinned against heaven and against you. I am no longer worthy to be called your son. "'

[22]"But the father said to his servants, 'Quick! Bring the best robe and put it on him. Put a ring on his finger and sandals on his feet. [23]Bring the fattened calf and kill it. Let's have a feast and celebrate. [24]For this son of mine was dead and is alive again; he was lost and is found.' So they began to celebrate.

[25]"Meanwhile, the older son was in the field. When he came near the house, he heard music and dancing. [26]So he called one of the servants and asked him what was going on. [27]'Your brother has come, 'he replied, 'and your father has killed the fattened calf because he has him back safe and sound.'

[28]"The older brother became angry and refused to go in. So his father went out and pleaded with him. [29]But he answered his father, 'Look! All these years I've been slaving for you and never disobeyed your orders. Yet you never gave me even a young goat so I could celebrate with my friends. [30]But when this son of yours who has squandered your property with prostitutes comes home, you kill the fattened calf for him!'

[31]" 'My son,' the father said, 'you are always with me, and everything I have is yours. [32]But we had to celebrate and be glad, because this brother of yours was dead and is alive again; he was lost and is found.' "